THE SURREY CRICKET QUIZ BOOK

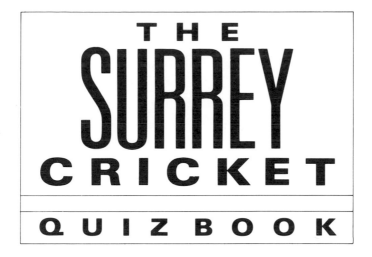

THE SURREY CRICKET
QUIZ BOOK

BOB CRAMPSEY

MAINSTREAM
PUBLISHING

First published in Great Britain in 1988 by
MAINSTREAM PUBLISHING COMPANY (EDINBURGH) LTD.
7 Albany Street
Edinburgh EH1 3UG

ISBN 1 85158 120 0 (paper)

British Library Cataloguing in Publication Data:

Crampsey, Robert A. (Robert Anthony), *1930-*
  The Surrey cricket quiz book.
  1. Surrey. County cricket. Clubs. Surrey
  County Cricket Club, to 1987
  I. Title
  796.35′863′094221

ISBN 1-85158-120-0

Typeset in Times by Pulse Origination, Edinburgh.
Printed and bound in Great Britain by
Butler & Tanner Ltd, Frome and London

*To the habitués of the lower landing
at THE OVAL.*

Contents

LONDON PRIDE
— SURREY COUNTY CRICKET CLUB

Surrey cricket teams have taken the field for more than a century and a half now, and this book is in a sense a history of Surrey County Cricket in question form. Surrey county sides have been playing at The Oval for almost all that time and of course there were Surrey sides in the free-ranging days before that, but this book will take the move to The Oval as the starting-point and very largely concentrate on the more formalised cricket which followed in the wake of the setting-up of the county championship.

The history of Surrey divides fairly comfortably and conveniently into five distinct stages. In the 1880s and 1890s, it was the time of the great bowlers, of Richardson and Lohmann and, a little later "Razor" Smith, those bowlers making the running in the great Surrey side of that time which took the championship whole or in part in eight years out of nine. So smooth-running was this machine that it scarcely needed the services of a regular captain and in at least one of those seasons did not have them.

There were still fine bowlers aplenty in the fifteen years or so before the Kaiser's war, but somehow the batsmen began to occupy centre stage, the astonishingly prolific Tom Hayward, the perky Bobby Abel, surely with Bernard Constable much later on the epitome of Cockney resilience. There was Hayes who would not have been overshadowed at any other time and Jack Hobbs whose name perhaps more than anyone else's in the world is synonymous with top-class batsmanship and who met the last great test of genius in that he exhibited his consummate mastery across half a life-time. He was quiet in demeanour, impeccable in behaviour, living proof of the old tag that "all the Players are Gentlemen". His was a gift of a rare order, for he was capped by his aristocratic captain almost as soon as he padded up for the first time at The Oval.

It is noteworthy that the greatest batsman the county ever produced played only once between 1905 and 1934 in a championship-winning side and that was in the campaign of 1914 which was fractionally curtailed by the war that followed and which certainly robbed him of six of his most productive years. Since he himself thought that he was never as good a player after 1918, one can only feebly imagine what records he might have set had a peaceful solution been found in the August of 1914.

He was certainly good enough for any mortal man when cricket resumed in 1919 and for the next 20 years the Oval score-board seemed to revolve endlessly so that scores of 500, while still comparitively unusual, were not worthy of any great comment. It was not entirely a case of mammoth totals and all-run fives to the very edges of the vast playing area. Bowlers had their moments as well, but not too many despite the sterling work of such as Tom Rushby and M. J. C. Allom, with Alf Gover supplying perseverance and hostility as the next war hove into view. "Bosser" Martin's pitches broke bowlers' hearts and Kennington Oval was not the easiest ground on which to win games — indeed losing them often took a bit of doing as well.

Hobbs was back in 1979 and so too was Andrew Sandham, the perfect straight man, who would have been a star attraction with almost any other county. Runs flowed from him in a torrent yet he was always and uncomplainingly overshadowed by the presence at the other end. The highly-gifted amateurs Knight and Crawford reappeared. Such appearances were somewhat irregular but their skills blazed like meteors. Unlike some other of the southern counties, Surrey's dependence on amateurs has always been comparatively restricted, there have been few of the colourful if ineffective eccentrics who have so brightened Somerset cricket for example. Surrey was a more business-like enterprise. There were amateurs with the traditional dash of the cavalier, it is true. Percy Fender was an outstanding player who made thousands of runs and took hundreds of wickets, to say nothing of his catches. His astute brain furnished proof that cricket is the only game in which captaincy matters a damn but that there it is crucial. It was and is a standing rebuke to the game's administrators at the highest level that personal animus prevented him from ever captaining England, a task for which he was so abundantly equipped.

Another Surrey amateur of the time, Freddie Brown, would captain England with the traditional panache and swagger of the amateur although not for another 20 years, but there was little of the quixotic about the man who was the most celebrated of the county's inter-war amateurs.

Douglas Jardine may have favoured a Harlequin's cap when batting but that was almost his only concession to frivolity. He made his preparations for cricket with a thoroughness which no Yorkshire professional ever surpassed and he conceived it to be his duty to remove as many of the game's glorious uncertainties as prudent pre-planning could manage. It is fair to say that he was perhaps widely-esteemed and respected rather than deeply-loved. He would have been very much at home in the snarling Test arenas of recent years.

As I say, bowlers had to acquire a certain pragmatism and sense of reality in an era when there could be 500 on the board half an hour before the close and double centuries were excellent but not world-shattering. The foot soldiers, the heroes of any county, slogged it out uncomplainingly; Eddie Watts was capable of short spells of great fieriness and T. H. Barling was the epitome of the professional county cricketer. His name was scarcely familiar to anyone outside Surrey ranks and yet he was numbered among those who have scored 20,000 runs and taken around 1000 wickets and that is a rather select band.

The Second World War was a very different affair from the First, and right from the start The Oval was commandeered. Dug up, barbed-wired and concrete-posted it seems impossible when one looks at the photographs of 1944 that it could ever have been used for first-class cricket again. It was though, and in time for the prompt restart of the 1946 season. That 1946 side was a strange mixture of the pre and post-war. Players like Gover, Parker, Fishlock and Barling soldiered on while in came the Romulus and Remus of Kennington Oval, the Bedsers, Alec and Eric. In the case of the first-named it was immediately apparent that a major world talent had been unearthed. One by one the new boys came into the side: Laker, Lock, Constable.

For those who had been away, just to be playing again was everything. Surrey County Cricket Club is enormously in the debt of those such as pre-war captain E. R. T. Holmes who deferred his playing retirement for two or three years until a definite successor could be found. The game was in a boom period; attendances of 10,000 at The Oval for run of the mill county matches were commonplace and Surrey in the championship were usually there or thereabouts.

At the beginning of the 1952 season something happened which explains why ordinary cricketers fantasise about themselves in the first-class game. In a stroke of surpassing vision Stuart Surridge was appointed as captain. It was the bravest of appointments because he had no great track record as a player. Throughout his career he would never be considered for an England place although he regularly took wickets and could make useful lower-order runs. More surprisingly, at a time when amateur bowlers were thin on the deck (from about 1954 onwards) and any aspiring undergraduate could and almost always did get a peg in the Gentlemen's dressing-room for the Players match, no such invitation came the way of Surridge. He had to be content with such minor distinctions as winning the county championship five times in a row — no one had ever done that before. Far beyond that, he never knew what it was to captain a county side which did not win the championship.

His detractors, and the ungenerous are always legion, point to his attack of the two Bedsers, Laker, Lock, Peter Loader a little later, and say that anyone could have captained this side. They point out that Surrey could afford to let such a perfectly good spinner as J. W. McMahon go. This is to miss the point. Surridge was a galvanising demon of a captain whose instinct for declarations savoured of sorcery. Once Parker and Fishlock retired, which they did after the first pennant, he was not, with the exception of Peter May, over-burdened with world-class batsmen. Micky Stewart and Ken Barrington were actually able to learn their trade and win titles simultaneously.

Initially the crowds at The Oval loved it all. Kennington crowds have always been been cheerfully partisan, very much the locals supporting their team. Lord's for all its imposing grandeur relies inevitably much more on the passing trade. In that regard it is the St

Andrews of the cricket world. Surridge's achievements probably reached their peak in 1956 when for the first time in almost half a century the Australian touring side fell to a county side and that by the resounding margin of ten wickets.

The example Surridge set and his insistence on keenness and effort carried over into the first two years of Peter May's captaincy and the younger man's industry and pleasant leadership saw the championships of 1957 and 1958 secured. Then came a swift and shattering decline. After the 1958 tour of Australia and New Zealand Peter May never quite seemed to recapture his verve and enthusiasm for the game and understandably became pre-occupied with the longer-term business of making a living, which at that time was not afforded by the game even to professionals on any acceptable scale.

Quite apart from this, Surrey had done something which in sport contained the certain seeds of disaster. Put starkly, they had become too good for the opposition. Attendances were to plummet in the 1960s and 1970s, but this had already started to happen towards the end of the championship run. This was because home wins had become sure things and one of the great charms of cricket, uncertainty of outcome, had largely been removed. Fifteen thousand spectators became five thousand and then dwindled to a few hundred disconsolate souls sparsely sprinkled throughout the cavernous recesses of The Oval.

All too often the glamour players, Alec Bedser, May, Lock and Laker were off on Test duty and the fact that the excellent replacements Clark, Constable, Eric Bedser, Fletcher and Cox did so well only served to reinforce the notion that Surrey had distanced themselves totally from the competition.

Historians of the game may well come to see the ten years between 1962-1972 as one of the darkest pages in cricket's chronicles. First-class cricket was bankrupt not only financially but apparently of ideas; the county programme was dwindling and there seemed no clear notion of what to put in its place. The solutions arrived at did not help Surrey greatly at first. The overseas signings were not uniformly unsuccessful, Intikhab Alam was a useful acquisition in anybody's terms, but there were no megastars such as other counties had attracted. The Oval supporter could find no immediate equivalent of Kanhai, Sobers, the Richards (Barry and Viv), Lloyd, Zaheer or D'Oliveira. Nor did the county show the aptitude for the one-day game which was to transform the fortunes of Lancashire, Somerset and Sussex. The very size of The Oval was dispiriting and the frequent rumours as to the scope or even existence of redevelopment plans did nothing to create the necessary climate of confidence.

The sad outcome was that such fine players and county stalwarts as David Sydenham, Robin Jackman and Arnold Long played almost throughout their home careers to a comparative handful of spectators and the loss was perhaps even greater when one thinks of the talents of John Edrich, Micky Stewart and Pat Pocock. The odd flash of lightning relieved the gloom, the championship win in 1971, the Benson and Hedges Cup triumph three years afterwards, but these were isolated occurrences and the county seemed to have settled for a comfortable but anonymous middle of the table role. Delightful cricketing oddities, such as F. J. Titmus turning out for Surrey in the twilight of his career, were of little consolation when one thought back to the great days of the 1950s.

One can see now that the Packer crisis, though painful and distasteful, was perhaps the emetic of which first-class cricket in this country stood in need. At The Oval the great ground was slowly transformed, all the more important in that Surrey had never been notable for taking the game round the county. Within its boundaries there are no equivalents of Tunbridge Wells, Bath or Cheltenham. It had become unclear whether the great pavilion was a national monument or a mausoleum. It is a marvellous building to be in with its magnificent collection of pictures, photographs, score cards and cricket memorabilia. One feels part of the history of the game and there is no better place for experiencing that wonderful sense of the game's continuity; in the old phrase "you can hear the ghosts walk". At the same time it had to be conceded that it was a warren of passages and big draughty rooms. Something had to be done for the comfort of non-members for whom The Oval was an extremely cheerless place right up until the end of the 1960s. The customers simply would not come any longer to sit on wooden backless benches and take whatever an English summer might care to throw at them.

The Oval had to be modernised, and to date it has been renovated well. It was unthinkable that the ground which pioneered Test cricket in England in 1880 should be lost to the game at highest level. It was the ground which had seen the Ashes regained in 1926 and 1963 after long periods of Australian ascendancy, the ground on which Hutton had scored 364 and batted through an entire innings for a double century against the 1950 West Indians. It was the ground on which Jessop had played his memorable knock and on which Bradman, eyes smarting from the tumultuous reception given him on his last appearance, had been bowled second ball by a delivery from Eric Hollies which it may be doubted if he ever saw. Constantine had played a hectic innings there for West Indies in 1939 as lightning flickered around the sky in a portent of what lay ahead, and in very truth every overseas player of calibre had exhibited his skills in that setting. Gavaskar almost won a match for India against long odds and the Chappell brothers made of an England-Australia Test match a unique family occasion.

So good will towards the club was certainly not lacking. The return of Mickey Stewart as cricket manager brought a welcome whiff of professionalism back to the ground. Players once more began to look like county cricketers on parade and off, and improvement in appearance brought about a gradual recovery in self-confidence. Captains still tended to be appointed too late in their careers, or mysteriously lost form once appointed, but there was the distinct impression that the ship was in the process of being righted.

Yet, if like myself you prefer county cricket to the one-day game or even to Test matches (and there are more of us than might be thought) one's last thoughts of The Oval must surely be for those players thought to be short of Test Class, (that mysterious quality in which David Steele of Northants was so long judged to be deficient), who are the very cement of the three-day game. I think of Bernie Constable, neat in everything he did, of the persevering David Sydenham, of Robin Jackman for whom no cause was ever lost, of good players such as Ron Tindall and Mike Willett who in the days of surpassing Surrey strength found it so hard to establish themselves in the first eleven on a regular basis. I think of the fine cricketers like Richard Jefferson and Dudley Owen-Thomas (the country's best judges could scarcely have been right about him in

15

1972 and wrong in 1975) who left the game very prematurely in that very bad decade of which I wrote earlier.

The game has lost none of its old capacity to stir and delight. One need look back no further than the Surrey v. Somerset match of 1987 at The Oval when after three see-saw days the last over began with all three results still possible. On the last ball Somerset could have won or Surrey saved the match. Indeed had Somerset chosen to invoke the two-minute rule, Graham Clinton, courageously batting with a broken hand, would never have been able to survive the one ball he faced.

I will feel the pulse begin to race as I climb The Oval station escalator in 1988, hoping to see the sun shine through the glass canopy at the top. I shall sit out on the narrow first floor balcony which is the only place from which to watch Surrey cricket, and if the crowd is small we will still know that we are uniquely blessed.

Till then, I hope these questions interest you when rain stops play or the nights of winter close in and may your cricket watching be happy.

Questions

1 Who was the president of the MCC who in 1883 took 8-41 for Kent against Surrey at The Oval?

2 Who scored 204 and did the hat-trick against Sussex in 1885?

3 How is this player commemorated at The Oval?

4 Who captained Surrey before the First World War, was President just before the Second World War and was made a Freeman of Scarborough?

5 Who was the Surrey wicket-keeper who, on tour in New Zealand, was imprisoned for an alleged assault over a bet?

6 What was his great wicket-keeping achievement in 1868?

7 In what peculiar way is a dismissal of J. Southerton recorded in the score book?

8 Who took all ten Australian wickets in an innings when playing for the Players against the first Australian side of 1878 at The Oval?

9 Who was the first player in first-class cricket to score a double century and perform the hat-trick in the same match?

10 Who was the Yorkshireman who took 8-40 for Surrey against Yorkshire at The Oval in 1888?

MORE EARLY DAYS

11 The great Surrey bowler W. H. Lockwood qualified by residence. Which first-class county missed him?

12 What very rare batting feat did H. Jupp accomplish against Yorkshire at The Oval in 1874?

13 A Surrey player is the only person ever to have been given a Test Match as a benefit. Who was he?

14 Did Tom Hayward ever "bag a pair"?

15 Was Tom Richardson's 10-45 against Essex at The Oval in 1894 regarded as first-class?

16 Which two Surrey captains won the championship in their first two years?

17 Who was the Australian bowler who took 10-29 against Surrey in 1899?

18 Which famous batsman did he dismiss for a pair?

19 When Surrey won the 1914 championship, how many of their games were left unplayed as a result of the outbreak of war?

20 Who obtained permission for Surrey County Cricket Club to adopt as a badge the Prince of Wales' feathers?

TOM HAYWARD

21 What was the occupation of his father?

22 What other famous Surrey cricketer's father was a Cambridge groundsman?

23 What record did Tom Hayward establish between 16 April and 31 May 1900?

24 How long was he with Surrey and when did he finish?

25 In what year did he do the double?

26 What distinguished his batting in the 1906 season?

27 What unusual bowling feat did he perform in 1899?

28 Did he ever score 3000 runs in a season?

29 What was his top score?

30 Who was his partner and who were the opponents in the record fourth-wicket stand of 448 in 1899?

BEFORE THE KAISER

31 Who was the Warwickshire player, first-name initials W. G., who made 124 and 109 against Surrey at The Oval in 1913?

32 Who was the Surrey player who was involved in two tied matches, once as an umpire?

33 Who was the Essex pace bowler who took 13-64 against Surrey at Leyton in 1893?

34 Who was the Hollywood film star who as a boy often went to watch Surrey at The Oval, his neighbourhood cricket ground?

35 Why was D. L. A. Jephson known as "The Lobster"?

36 W. H. Lockwood performed the double for Surrey in 1900. Who was the next Oval player to achieve this?

37 Who was the Surrey bowler who took 13-51 against Lancashire in a match which was over in a day in 1888?

38 What was the Lancashire aggregate score in this match?

39 What was the name of the Middlesex bowler who in 1885 took all ten wickets for 59 in the first innings of The Oval match?

40 What pre-First World War Sussex captain became a Hollywood film star?

HITCH AND SMITH

41 Complete the following limerick:
If I were enormously rich
I would build a cathedral in which
I would make me a shrine of a noble design . . .

42 With what county did Bill Hitch become associated as coach?

43 For which club in the Lancashire League did he play?

44 How many centuries did he score?

45 On how many Australian tours did he go?

46 What notable innings did he play against the Australians at The Oval in 1921?

47 In which match in 1905 did Razor Smith and Tom Rushby bowl unchanged for an entire innings?

48 How many wickets did Smith take in 1910 — 100, 200, 250?

49 He had a field day against Northants at The Oval. What was his match analysis?

50 What was his occupation in the winter?

JACK HOBBS

51 When did he first play for Surrey?

52 How many century partnerships did he have in Tests with Herbert Sutcliffe?

53 Who was batting with Jack Hobbs when he equalled the record number of centuries scored by Dr W. G. Grace?

54 How many times in Jack Hobbs' career with Surrey did the county win the championship?

55 Jack Hobbs never had a pair in first-class cricket. Of which other great batsman could that be said?

56 Against Lancashire in 1912 he put on 135 in 90 minutes for the first wicket with Tom Hayward. How many of those did Hobbs make?

57 Which county refused him a trial?
58 How many centuries did he hit against Australia?
59 What caused him to miss almost the entire season of 1921?
60 How often did he score 3000 runs in a season?

JACK HOBBS AGAIN

61 How many benefits did Jack Hobbs receive with Surrey?
62 How old was he when he played his highest-ever innings?
63 How many did he make and where?
64 What honour befell him in 1953?
65 Against which county was he least successful?
66 What was his last score for Surrey?
67 He was the second person to score 50,000 runs in first-class cricket. Who had been the first?
68 How many wickets did he take in his career?
69 What was his best bowling performance?
70 What was his best bowling performance in the county championship?

MORE ON SIR JACK

71 How many games did he play before being capped?
72 Which peer capped him?
73 When was the first time he exceeded 3000 runs?
74 How many hundreds did he have in that season?
75 What remarkable performance did he accomplish in the match with the Gentlemen at Scarborough in 1925?
76 When did he score his last first class 100?
77 Whose benefit match was it?
78 In what part of London was his sports shop?
79 To which promising schoolboy did he present a bat in recognition of an outstanding performance for Tonbridge?
80 Hobbs played against both W. G. Grace and Don Bradman. True or false?

J. N. CRAWFORD

81 He was invited to play for Surrey while still at which school?

82 What astonishing bowling feat did he perform in 1904?
83 How often did he perform the double?
84 How many times was he chosen for England?
85 What was his haul in the 1907/8 series of Tests against Australia?
86 What unusual international distinction did he achieve?
87 Returning to Surrey after the war he was involved in a first-wicket stand of 96 in 32 minutes. Who was his partner?
88 Who were the opposition?
89 In the same year he took part in a stand of 80 for the last wicket against the Australian Imperial Forces. How many did he make?
90 Who was his partner?

P. G. H. FENDER

91 With which county did he begin his first-class career?
92 How many runs did he score and how many wickets did he take in first-class cricket?
93 How many times did he perform the double?
94 Against whom did he play his great innings of 113* in 42 minutes?
95 How many times did he take 100 wickets for Surrey?
96 In what years did he skipper the side?
97 What record did he achieve in 1920?
98 For whom did he score a century at Lord's in 1921?
99 How many caps did he win?
100 On which Test tour did he top the bowling average?

STRUDWICK AND SANDHAM

101 Where did Herbert Strudwick come from?
102 How long did he serve the county?
103 In his first-class career he had more than 1500 victims behind the stumps. True or false?
104 In how many Tests did he play?
105 What great distinction was conferred upon him after World War II?

106 How long was Andrew Sandham with Surrey as a player?

107 What was his highest score?

108 What was his outstanding performance against the 1934 Australians?

109 How many centuries did he score?

110 He made a century in his last county match. Where was it and when?

THE ROARING TWENTIES

111 Who was the Sussex and England player who appeared for Surrey in 1919?

112 Who was the Middlesex amateur who scored a century in the deciding county championship match with Surrey that year?

113 Who was the amateur leg-break bowler who came home on leave from the Gold Coast in 1924 and headed the county bowling averages?

114 Who were the opponents when Jack Hobbs and Andrew Sandham put on 428 for the first wicket in 1926?

115 In which match in 1928 did Surrey score 567 and fail to win first innings lead?

116 Who was the Lancashire batsman who in this match scored a triple ton?

117 What additional distinction did this innings confer on the batsman?

118 Who was the famous Surrey fast bowler who on his first county appearance at Horsham against Sussex took the wicket of A. F. Wensley who had made 97?

119 Who were the two bowlers who dismissed Glamorgan for 37 in 1929?

120 Who was the amateur who took most wickets for Surrey in 1930?

BETWEEN THE WARS (I)

121 Andrew Ducat belongs to what small select band of sportsmen?

122 How and when did he die?

123 How many times did Andrew Sandham score 1000 runs in a season?

124 How many century partnerships did he have with Jack Hobbs?

125 For how long was P. G. H. Fender captain of Surrey?

126 Percy Fender is still regarded as having scored the fastest genuine century in first-class cricket. When did he do this and against whom?

127 In 1927 at Lord's he established a world bowling record which lasted for 45 years. What was it and who surpassed it?

128 After Fender demitted office who were the three Oxford Blues who held the captaincy until the outbreak of World War II?

129 Who was the Surrey bowler who in 1936 (and 1937) took 200 wickets for the first time since Tom Richardson?

130 Which two players did Alan Peach recommend to Surrey in 1938?

BETWEEN THE WARS (2)

131 What was the name of the brothers who appeared as amateurs for Surrey and played on opposite sides in the 'Varsity match of 1919?

132 Two other well-known cricketing brothers also appeared on opposite sides in this match. Who were they?

133 Who was the son of the South African diamond millionaire who on occasions kept for Surrey between 1928-1930?

134 Who was the Surrey player who did the double in 1932 and failed by one wicket to repeat the feat 20 years later?

135 Who scored 168 in 130 minutes against Kent at Blackheath in 1932?

136 Against which county in 1932 did he get a double century at The Oval and a century in the return match?

137 Did he ever play for Surrey after World War II?

138 In which series did he first captain England?

139 What was the connection in 1935 between "Bosser" and leatherjackets?

140 What was the last first-class match played at The Oval before the outbreak of war in September 1939?

141 Who was the Test umpire who scored 77* for Hampshire at The Oval in 1937?

142 Who was the prominent sports journalist who turned out for Surrey in 1931?

143 Who took four wickets in four balls at Worcester in 1935?

144 How many of the Surrey players who played in the last pre-World War II match took part in the first post-war game in 1946?

145 Who was the Surrey batsman of the 1920s and 1930s who later became a umpire and at Worcester in 1938 no-balled E. L. McCormick of the Australian touring team on no fewer than 19 occasions in three overs?

146 Who was the South African whose century against Surrey in 1935 was one of three which he made in consecutive matches?

147 Who in 1939 took 10-67 in the Warwickshire second innings at Edgbaston?

148 Did he ever take 100 wickets in a season?

149 He was related to another Surrey player of that period. Which one?

150 What experiment was tried in the course of the 1939 season?

1938: AN AUSTRALIAN YEAR

151 Who was the Australian wicket-keeper who scored a century in the first of the two matches against Surrey in the 1938 tour?

152 Len Hutton made 364 in The Oval Test of 1938. Who were the other England centurions?

153 In this Test who was the Australian bowler with figures of 1-298 in the English innings?

154 Which two Australian batsmen were unable to bat in the second innings?

155 Who was the Surrey amateur whose off-spin took 5-27 against Essex at Westcliff in August?

156 Who had a match analysis of 9-79 against Surrey at Trent Bridge?

157 Who scored a double century against Somerset in the first home county match of 1938?

158 Who was the future England captain who took 11-135 in the next home match against Derbyshire?

159 What was special about the home match against Hampshire which began on 13 July 1938?

160 In E. W Brooks' benefit match at The Oval, Laurie Fishlock was out in a curious way against Kent. What happened?

THE LATE 1930s

161 Who had a match analysis of 13-103 against Warwickshire at The Oval in July 1937?

162 At The Oval against Yorkshire in August 1937, Laurie Fishlock became only the eighth cricketer in history to do what?

163 Who had been the last player to achieve this?

164 Who made 251 for once out against Yorkshire at The Oval in July 1938?

165 Who was the Lancashire leg-break bowler who returned a match-winning 6-53 in the match at the Oval in September 1938?

166 Who in the 1938 season took 14-85 against Worcestershire on the Kidderminster ground?

167 Who in 1938 were the two Yorkshire bowlers who bowled unchanged at Bramall Lane in dismissing Surrey in 22 overs?

168 Who finished off this match by taking 5-45 in the second innings with leg-breaks?

169 Who was the Oxford University player who in 1938 scored a century for the University against Surrey at The Oval?

170 Andrew Sandham retired in 1937. How many runs did he make in his career, 20,000, 30,000, 40,000?

L. B. FISHLOCK

171 In which edition of Wisden was he one of the Five Players of The Year?

172 For which amateur soccer club did he play when capped by England?

173 What was his professional soccer club?
174 How many tours of Australia did he make?
175 In what capacity was he originally engaged by Surrey?
176 When did he score his first century?
177 When did he make his Test debut?
178 What was his extraordinary batting feat against one county in 1937?
179 With two others he was the last to be picked for Australia in 1946. Who were the other late choices?
180 How many runs did he score in 1946?

THE WAR AND JUST AFTER

181 To what use was The Oval put during the war?
182 Did it sustain any damage?
183 When was the centenary of play starting at The Oval?
184 Which sport did Surrey turn down for The Oval in 1945?
185 Surrey played two one-day matches only in 1945. Who were their opposition?
186 And the venues of these matches?
187 R. T. Crawford, brother of J. N. and V. F. S., died just after the end of the war. For which county had he played?
188 What was the side called for which Keith Miller and D. K. Carmody appeared in the summer of 1945?
189 Did any Surrey players take part in the "Victory Tests" against Australia in 1945.
190 Which pre-war Surrey player and future England captain was a prisoner of war?

THE YEAR 1946

191 What unique event took place in the match against India in May 1946?
192 What was the other Indian achievement in this match?
193 Which Glamorgan Test Player got his first championship century against Surrey at Cardiff?
194 Which Gloucester spinner had 13 Surrey wickets for 127 at Cheltenham?

195 Who had a match analysis of 7-91 and scored 86 and 102 v. Kent at Blackheath?

196 Against which county did Laurie Fishlock have two centuries in the one match?

197 Against which county did A. V. Bedser take 11-89 and end up losing?

198 Which Middlesex pair put on 296 for the third wicket at Lord's?

199 Against which county did Alec Bedser have a spell of 7-11?

200 Which county scored more than 500 against Surrey?

MORE OF 1946

201 When Somerset scored over 500 at Weston how many Surrey first team players were missing?

202 Who scored the first post-war century at The Oval?

203 What were the sides in the special match to mark the centenary of play at The Oval?

204 Who was the only non-Test player in the Old England side?

205 Who was the Essex spinner who took 11-119 at The Oval in June 1946?

206 What two batsmen put on 270 for Essex in a record first-wicket stand?

207 Which two Surrey players scored maiden centuries against Kent at The Oval?

208 Who was the extremely distinguished guest who attended the Bank Holiday match against Nottinghamshire in August 1946?

209 What was his connection with Surrey?

210 What was unusual about the century that Eric Bedser scored against Hampshire?

PLAY RESUMES AFTER HITLER

211 What was the career span of Stan Squires?

212 How many runs did he make for Surrey, 10,000, 15,000, 25,000?

213 How many first-class centuries did he score?

214 What was Stuart Surridge's off-field job?

215 Who got his county cap in 1948 for taking 6-7 in 6.3 overs in the match against Northants?

216 Which England captain scored 166 for Worcestershire at Worcester in May?

217 Which two Yorkshire bowlers bowled unchanged through the Surrey first innings in the match at Sheffield?

218 Who was the Yorkshire bowler who took 4-73 against Surrey at Bradford in July in his first county match?

219 In the Surrey v. Somerset match at The Oval in 1951 two bowlers took 11 wickets in the match, one on each side. Who were they?

220 The 1952 match against Kent at The Oval brought personal landmarks for Peter May and Stuart Surridge. What were they?

1947—THE SUNSHINE YEAR

221 Who was the South African captain who scored a century in May against Surrey at The Oval in the South Africans' second innings?

222 Who was the Glamorgan off-break bowler who took 9-97 in the second innings at Cardiff in August?

223 In which match did Jim Laker take 8-69 in the first innings and finish on the losing side?

224 What was unusual about his bowling in this innings?

225 What England Test batsman made his highest-ever score to date against Surrey in the match at Old Trafford?

226 Who was the England captain who scored his first-ever championship century against Surrey at Lord's.

227 What was the Surrey total in the Bank Holiday match at Trent Bridge?

228 How many Surrey batsmen made centuries in this total?

229 What was particularly noteworthy about Fletcher's innings?

230 Who was the Surrey bowler who made his maiden century in the match against Somerset at Taunton in September 1947?

231 Who had a match analysis of 12-92 against Somerset at The Oval in May?

232 Who was the Gloucestershire spinner who had a haul of 11-168 against Surrey at The Oval in June?

233 Who made his first team debut for Surrey against Oxford University in a two day match at The Oval in July 1947?

234 Who was the leg-break bowler who took 7-84 in the Surrey second innings in the match against Kent in July?

235 In the same month who scored a double century against Derbyshire?

236 And which Surrey bowler in that same match took 11-101?

237 In the match against Yorkshire at The Oval, the visitors were without Hutton, Yardley and Sellers. Who was the Yorkshire captain?

238 Which Yorkshireman hit his maiden century in this match? Two clues: he played for England and subsequently for another county.

239 Who was the Cambridge captain who hit his maiden championship century for Nottinghamshire in the August Bank Holiday game at The Oval?

240 In the Middlesex match at The Oval which of the visitors scored a century and took 12-174 in the course of the game?

1948—THE DON'S FAREWELL

241 In the May match against Surrey, Bradman scored 146. Who were the two other Australians who scored centuries?

242 Who carried his bat in the Surrey first innings?

243 Which Surrey bowler conceded more than 200 runs in 42 overs?

244 Which two Australians scored centuries in both the matches against Surrey?

245 How many balls did Don Bradman face in his last Test at the Oval?

246 How was he out?

247 Wht was the statistical effect of this dismissal?

248 Who was the Surrey player who got a pair in the Fifth Test?

249 Who top-scored for England in both innings?

250 Who fell just short of a double century for Australia in this Test and how was he dismissed?

1948—THE COUNTY SCENE

251 Who was the Derbyshire bowler who did the hat-trick against Surrey at Lord's?

252 Who were his victims?

253 Who took 11-91 against Derbyshire at Chesterfield in August?

254 Who was the 50-year-old Glamorgan player who took 10-66 in the match against Surrey at Cardiff?

255 Who was the Surrey spin bowler who had a match analysis of 10-150 against Hampshire at Bournemouth in August?

256 Who scored a double century against Leicestershire in the away match?

257 Who was the mighty hitter who had a match analysis of 10-122 for Middlesex at Lord's?

258 On Whitsun Bank Holiday Monday there was a record crowd at Trent Bridge for the game against Surrey. How many spectators attended?

259 Who was the Surrey captain who scored 132 in the first innings of this match?

260 Surrey finished in second position in the championship, four points behind the winners. Who were champions in 1948?

MORE DOINGS OF 1948

261 Who was the Surrey batsman who retired having made almost 20,000 runs since 1927?

262 Who took 8-55 in the first innings of the Gloucestershire match at The Oval?

263 What was unusual about this match?

264 Who was the Lancashire dentist and England Test player who took 7-43 in the Surrey second innings at The Oval?

31

265 Who were the Surrey openers who put on 226 for the first wicket against Oxford University at Guildford in June?

266 Who was the England Test cricketer who had the hat-trick against Surrey at The Oval and also had the highest score of the match?

267 Which county did Surrey defeat twice within a week for the second year in succession?

268 Who hit his first county century for Yorkshire against Surrey at The Oval? Clue: he was a future Yorkshire captain.

269 In this match Arthur McIntyre was hurt and Yorkshire allowed him to be replaced by another wicket-keeper. Who took over?

270 Who was the Middlesex bowler who took 14-97 in Stan Squires' benefit match?

THE 1949 SEASON

271 Surrey defeated the county champions three times in county matches. How was this possible?

272 In which match did Laurie Fishlock make more than twice the opposition second innings total and Jim Laker have a match analysis of 9-80?

273 Who had a double century against Derbyshire at The Oval in May?

274 Who were the two Surrey bowlers who bowled unchanged to dismiss Derbyshire in 30 overs in their first innings?

275 In which match at The Oval did one brother score 132 and the other take 6-65?

276 What was remarkable about J. K. Graveney's bowling performance?

277 A Surrey bowler making his debut had 5-51 in the Gloucestershire second innings. Who was he?

278 Who was the Oxford University bowler who in seven overs and at a cost of five runs dismissed Whittaker, Eric Bedser, Parker and McIntyre?

279 Name the four future county captains who appeared in the Cambridge side at Guildford in June 1949?

280 Who hit his maiden century for Surrey in this match and who

was the reserve wicket-keeper who held six catches in the University's first innings?

MORE FROM 1949

281 Who put on 260 for the first wicket against Somerset at The Oval in July 1949?
282 Who was the Surrey captain who scored the first century of the season at The Oval against Kent?
283 Who was the Yorkshire bowler who ended on the losing side with match figures of 12-122?
284 In the Bank Holiday game at The Oval against Notts which Surrey player recorded his highest career score for the second time in a month?
285 What was noteworthy about Middlesex's defeat at The Oval in August?
286 Who was the Surrey player in this match who scored his maiden county century?
287 Who was the Warwickshire bowler who took 11-76 in the last Oval match of the season?
288 How many wickets did he take against Surrey in the season?
289 Who was the future England captain with a Liverpool connection who made 130 for Sussex at Hove in August 1949?
290 Who performed the hat-trick in each innings against Surrey that month?

1950—A CALYPSO YEAR

291 In the first match against Surrey at The Oval two West Indians made centuries in the first innings. Who were they?
292 Who made a 100 for Surrey?
293 Who missed a century for Surrey by one run?
294 In the second game with the county, who was the Hampshire batsman who scored a century for the tourists?
295 And the other West Indies centurion in this match?
296 Who carried his bat for England in the Fifth Test at The Oval?
297 Which West Indian bowler had a match analysis of 10-160?
298 What Surrey player got a pair in this Test match?

299 How many amateurs were there in the England side?

300 Who were they?

1950—THE COUNTY SCENE

301 Who had a match analysis of 10-89 against Essex at Chelmsford?

302 Which Surrey batsman scored 1000 runs for the first time in his career?

303 Who was the Kent bowler who took 8-23 in the Surrey first innings in the match at Blackheath?

304 What was his match analysis?

305 In the Lancashire match at Old Trafford which home slow bowler celebrated the award of his county cap by taking 8-60 in the Surrey first innings?

306 Who was the Leicestershire bowler who performed the hat-trick at Leicester?

307 What was unusual about the Surrey first innings total of 275-9 against Notts at Trent Bridge with regard to the scoring?

308 In what way were the weather conditions unusual for the match against Somerset at Wells?

309 Who were the two cousins who took 19 of the 20 wickets which Surrey lost against Essex at The Oval?

310 Who was the Oxford University number eight batsman who made 92 in the first innings when a full-strength Surrey side was beaten at Guildford in June?

MORE OF 1950

311 Who scored his maiden first-class century against Cambridge University?

312 Who was the Yorkshire opener later with Warwickshire who scored 35 out of 149 on his debut for Yorkshire at The Oval in July 1950?

313 Who scored a century in his own benefit match in 1950?

314 Who scored a century for Middlesex in the same match?

315 Who in the last match of the season at The Oval took 12 wickets for 96 against Leicestershire?

316 What quick-scoring feat did Alec Bedser perform against Sussex at Hastings in August 1950?

317 Who took 11 wickets at seven runs each against Worcestershire?

318 In this match who was the Surrey amateur who scored a first-innings century?

319 Who was the England captain who scored a century against Surrey at Bramall Lane in July 1950?

320 What happened at The Oval on 4 October 1950 which had not taken place there since 1895?

THE YEAR 1951

321 Who made a century in both innings against Essex at Southend?

322 Which two Surrey bowlers put on 131 for the 8th wicket against Glamorgan at Cardiff?

323 In which match did Jim Laker perform the hat-trick?

324 Which Lancashire pace bowler had a match analysis of 9-62 at Manchester?

325 Who was the Leicestershire all-rounder who scored 130 in his side's only innings then took 6-23 in the Surrey first innings at Ashby-de-la-Zouch?

326 A Middlesex player, who in five seasons had never scored more then 54, made 102 batting number nine against Surrey at Lord's. Who was he?

327 Who, re-appearing as captain after two years' absence from the game, scored 34 and 54* against Northants at Kettering?

328 Who had a ninth wicket partnership of 161 against Glamorgan at The Oval?

329 Which visiting player carried his bat in Lancashire's first innings at The Oval?

330 What was noteworthy about Somerset's victory at The Oval in May 1951?

THE YEAR 1952—MOSTLY BOWLING

331 On which ground did Jim Laker return the astonishing bowling figures of 42-29-44-2?

332 And, more penetratingly, where did he bowl 11-5-15-6?

333 What Surrey player missed a double century at Leicester by three runs?

334 Who was the former Surrey player who took 6-42 for Northants against Surrey at Rushden?

335 Who won this match for Surrey with 7-57 in 31 overs?

336 What two bowlers bundled out Notts unchanged in 22.4 overs at Trent Bridge in June?

337 What two Surrey stalwarts retired at the end of 1952?

338 Only one county was unbeaten by Surrey in the 1952 championship, which was it?

339 Who was the reserve bowler who took 7-22 against Cambridge University and had a match analysis of 11-70?

340 Which university batsman scored a century in the second innings here?

1952 AND MOSTLY INDIANS

341 Why would Tony Lock remember India's victory at The Oval in July?

342 Who was the umpire on this occasion?

343 Which Indian bowler performed the hat-trick?

344 Why would Peter May also remember this match?

345 In the Test at The Oval what was the low point of India's first innings?

346 Who shared the Indian wickets in this first innings?

347 Who scored a century for England in The Oval Test?

348 Who put on 143 for the best opening stand against India?

349 What was the result of the first match between India and Surrey in May?

350 Who was the Indian bowler who in the first innings of this match returned figures of 13.3-3-20-5?

40s AND 50s

351 Which two Surrey players opened the bowling and the batting at Old Trafford in 1953 on the same day?

352 Which Surrey batsman was three times involved in a last-wicket century stand?

353 What was noteworthy about the first county match at The Oval of season 1953?

354 What were Alec Bedser's figures in this match?

355 Who was the player in the 1953 Surrey side who went to Kent?

356 Who was the 17-year-old who in 1953 took six Surrey wickets for 13 runs at Bristol?

357 Which two Surrey players were capped in 1953?

358 Who was the off-spinner who in 1954 had a match-winning 7-23 for Glamorgan against Surrey?

359 Which team in 1954 lost by an innings at The Oval in a county match which lasted just over 5 hours?

360 Who took 6-5 in the match?

JUST BEFORE THE CHAMPIONSHIP

361 Who were the Cambridge opening pair who put on 161 at Guildford in June?

362 What feat did Len Hutton accomplish at The Oval in July 1951?

363 The Yorkshire captain also scored a century that day. Who was he?

364 Who were the two Northants left-handers who made centuries at The Oval in the county match of 1951?

365 Who scored his first county century for Yorkshire against Surrey at Leeds in June?

366 In 1952 at Trent Bridge, Alec Bedser posted two notable milestones in the same innings. What were they?

367 Who had a match analysis of 7-23 against Derbyshire including 6-16 in their first innings against Surrey?

368 Who was the radio commentator who took 4-27 and 2-15 for Warwickshire?

369 Who was the Sheffield United goalkeeper who took 6-43 against Surrey at Leeds?

370 Around this time, if Surrey had been playing at Coalville who would their opponents have been?

371 What Leicestershire bowler took 8-7 against Surrey in 1955?

372 What Yorkshire bowler that year took 7-29 in Arthur McIntyre's benefit match?

373 Who scored 112 against Surrey at The Oval in his first match against his old county, also in 1955?

374 Who was the Scotland player who in 1955 took four wickets in 15 balls for Kent at The Oval?

375 Still in 1955, what was the sensational start to the Middlesex match at The Oval?

376 Who carried his bat in the Middlesex second innings?

377 Who in the match took 13 Middlesex wickets?

378 Which prominent Surrey player did not face the Australians at all in 1956?

379 Who was the Hampshire player, better known as a batsman, who took six wickets against Surrey at Portsmouth in 1956?

380 Which Surrey batsman in that season got to within ten runs of a double century in two successive matches?

381 In which season did he first appear for Surrey?

382 Which public school did he attend?

383 In which season was he named Cricketer of the Year?

384 He was the first captain ever to win five championships in a row. Who were the two who had recorded four successive wins previously?

385 What was noteworthy about the championship season of 1955?

386 In which season did he take more than fifty catches?

387 How many first-class wickets did he take, 250, 500, 750?

388 What innovation did he introduce in away matches?

389 He led Surrey 170 times altogether. How many of those games were won?

390 And lost?

391 In what capacity was Ken Barrington brought to Surrey?

392 When was he first capped for England?

393 He was dropped after that series, how long did he wait for a recall?

394 How many Test centuries did he make at home and abroad?

395 What unique Test batting achievement does he hold?

396 How many wickets did he take in his career, 80, 200, 500?

397 In 1965 he made 137 against New Zealand at Edgbaston. How many did he make in the next Test?

398 In 1962-63 he scored 1451 runs at 85.35 on the Australian tour. Only one English player has ever done better. Who was that?

399 His Test average against Australia is 63.96. Only one English player has bettered that. Who is he?

400 He scored 31,714 runs but oddly failed to score a century against no fewer than four counties. What were they?

THE LOCKS, TONY AND BERT

401 How many times did Tony Lock take 200 wickets in a season?

402 Did he ever take all ten wickets in an innings?

403 His bowling action became suspect for a time. What is reckoned to have caused this?

404 What was the name of the umpire who called him for throwing?

405 For which first-class county had the umpire played?

406 Groundsman Herbert C. Lock had an unusual middle name. What was it?

407 In addition to being Surrey groundsman Bert Lock was also on the books of Surrey. Did he ever play for the first team?

408 In the autumn of 1945, The Oval was a shambles with concrete posts embedded in the soil and hundreds of yards of barbed-wire fencing. Lock started the work of recovery on 8 October. When was the pitch ready?

409 How many turves were used for relaying and where were they obtained?

410 What national post was given to him when he ceased to be head groundsman at The Oval?

TWO OPENERS CLARK AND PARKER

411 For which League football clubs did Tom Clark play?
412 For how long was he a member of the Surrey first team?
413 What was his highest score for the county?
414 How many runs did he make and how many centuries?
415 Was Jack Parker ever capped for England?
416 In the years 1946 and 1947 he brought off something extremely unusual in county cricket. What was it?
417 What was his highest score in first-class cricket?
418 What was his career aggregate in runs?
419 How many wickets did he take?
420 He first played for Surrey in 1932. When did he make his first century?

THE HEAVENLY TWINS, THE BEDSERS

421 Where were the Bedsers, Alec and Eric, born?
422 How long was Alec on the books at The Oval?
423 How many times did he take 100 wickets?
424 In Stuart Surridge's first year as captain, Eric became one of the Surrey openers. Who was his usual partner?
425 Did either of the twins play for Surrey pre-war?
426 At what great event were they present in 1940?
427 How many wickets did Alec take in each of his first two Tests?
428 What record did he set on his Test debut?
429 What were their outstanding bowling contributions to the defeat of Middlesex at Lord's in August 1949?
430 How was it possible to tell which of them was at the crease?

P. B. H. MAY

431 In how many Tests did Peter May play?
432 He appeared in 52 consecutive Tests and equalled whose record?

433 How many Test centuries did he score?

434 He obtained two and a half Blues at Cambridge. What were the non-cricketing ones?

435 With his brother John he took the Kinnaird Cup three years running from 1951 to 1953. For what is this awarded?

436 Whom did he succeed as captain?

437 How many championships were won during his captaincy?

438 Against which newspaper did he raise a libel action after one of its reporters had criticised his attitude towards the club?

439 How many times did he captain England?

440 Peter May played for a soccer side which won the FA Amateur Cup, although he was not in the finals. What was the side?

BERNARD CONSTABLE

441 What distinction did Bernard Constable have?

442 When did he make his debut for Surrey?

443 When did he play his first county match?

444 When did he hit his first century?

445 What did he join the Surrey staff as?

446 Against which county did he score a double century in 1952?

447 Where was he born?

448 When did he join the Surrey staff?

449 Against which county did he score a century in two matches in 1961?

450 With Jim Laker he did most to achieve a Surrey win against the Australians of 1956. Laker took all ten wickets, what was Constable's contribution?

JOHN EDRICH

451 With which minor county did he start?

452 He was one of the powerful Edrich cricketing family. His cousin Bill of Middlesex and England was the most famous but how many others in the family played first-class cricket?

453 What was his first century at top level?

454 When did he have his initial first team game for Surrey?

455 What were his scores in the first match he was tried as an opener?

456 When did he get his first Test century?

457 How many Tests did he play in?

458 How many first-class centuries did he make in the course of his whole career?

459 In the 1965 season he set a record with a total of how many runs from nine consecutive innings?

460 In those nine innings he averaged 218.5. How many centuries were there in this run?

JIM LAKER'S FIFTEEN

461 Jim Laker lost his Surrey membership and that of MCC after the publication of which of his books?

462 With which club was he playing when spotted by Surrey?

463 In which famous match did he take eight wickets for two runs?

464 With which Bradford League club had he played pre-war?

465 When did he make his first appearance for Surrey?

466 When did he make his Test debut?

467 In which of his early Tests did he make top score?

468 What notable bowling feat did he perform against South Africa in the Oval Test of 1951?

469 Has any other bowler ever taken 19 wickets in a first-class match?

470 Did he ever go on an Australian tour?

471 How many years did he spend with Surrey?

472 How many times did he take 100 wickets?

473 For which other county did he play as an amateur?

474 How many first-class runs did he make, 3000, 5000, 10,000?

475 How many first-class centuries did he score?

THE 1960S

476 Who won the *Evening Standard* award for the fastest first-day century in the county championship in 1962?

477 What Australian state did Tony Lock play for?

478 For which minor county did Tom Clark play before joining Surrey?

479 Who left the county in the 1960s, asked to be re-instated but was turned down?

480 Ken Barrington came from Reading way. Can you name three other Surrey stalwarts who came from the same area?

481 When was Peter May's last full season?

482 Who was capped in 1962 having first played for Surrey in 1955?

483 Who succeeded Peter May as captain in 1963?

484 Who was the Football League goalkeeper who was named Man of the Match in a Gillette Cup match in which Surrey played?

485 Of which county did Surrey request a change of venue in 1963?

STILL WITH THE SWINGING, SPINNING SIXTIES

486 Who was the left-arm quick bowler who retired at the end of the 1966 season?

487 Which three prominent players retired at the end of season 1963?

488 When did Ken Barrington retire?

489 Who joined Surrey from Cambridge University in 1969?

490 Which two players were capped in 1964?

491 Who was the Surrey bowler who joined Kent and later became an umpire?

492 Which batsman, who joined the county in 1949 but did not establish himself until ten years later, scored 1800 runs in 1964?

493 When did Tony Lock join Leicestershire?

494 Who were the Surrey pair who put on 369 for the second wicket against New Zealand in the Third Test at Headingley?

495 The same pair figured in a third wicket stand of 225 at The Oval. Against whom?

AROUND THE 1970S

496 Which Surrey player was made Young Cricketer of the Year in 1972 and left county cricket in 1975?

497 Who was the Yorkshire player who took 4-24 and then made 50* in the J. P. L. match at Middlesbrough in August 1973?

498 What did Intikhab Alam and Robin Jackman most improbably do in the J. P. L. match against Yorkshire at The Oval in June 1974?

499 In the same competition a month later at The Oval who took 5-26 v. Surrey, made 50 and still was on the losing side?

500 Which two bowlers in total bowled 16 overs for 26 against Glamorgan at The Oval?

501 Who took 5-15 against Lincolnshire at Lincoln in the Gillette Cup?

502 Why was defeat by Somerset in the quarter-final of the Gillette Cup specially hard to bear?

503 Which Somerset player was named Man of the Match?

504 Which Surrey batsman took 4-10 in 10 overs against Cambridge University at Fenners in 1976?

505 Whose analysis for Glamorgan of 11-3-12-4 at Cardiff in the Benson and Hedges match still was not good enough?

MAY AND STEWART

506 What did the initials stand for in P. B. H. May?

507 He had an unusual batting distinction in 1951 which cannot now be equalled. What was it?

508 How many runs did he make in the 1951 season?

509 Who coached him when he was at Charterhouse?

510 Against which county did he score a double century while a Cambridge freshman?

511 What was Mickey Stewart's astonishing fielding achievement of 1957?

512 He had one outstanding individual fielding performance. What?

513 He scored a century in his second first-class match for Surrey. Who provided the opposition in that match in 1954?

514 For which Football League side did he play?

515 For which important football match was he rushed home from the West Indies but in fact arrived just too late to play?

516 Who were the Gloucestershire openers who put on 219 for the first wicket against Surrey at Bristol in September?

517 In which match did Geoff Arnold take the wickets of two Test batsmen with the first two balls of the match?

518 Which Surrey record did John Murray of Middlesex equal in the game at Lord's against Surrey?

519 Who was the Cambridge captain who made 115 for Surrey on his debut at The Oval against Middlesex?

520 Who retired from first-class cricket in 1975?

521 Who after 24 years in first-class cricket had the first hat-trick of his career for Leicestershire against Surrey at The Oval in July 1976?

522 Who were the Yorkshire batsmen who each scored a century in putting on 216 for the third wicket at The Oval?

523 Who took 11-110 in the match against Sussex at Hove (for Surrey)?

524 Who was the former Surrey spinner who took 6-40 in the Surrey first innings in that same match?

525 Who scored 242 for once out in the match against Worcester at Worcester?

526 Who was the Indian bowler who recorded a career-best performance in the tourists match against Surrey at The Oval in May?

527 What Surrey player made 111 v. Derbyshire at Chesterfield and then took three wickets for two runs in nine overs?

528 The same player scored 111 in another away match. Which one?

529 Who took in the match 10-116 against Surrey for Kent at Maidstone?

530 What was the unusual ending to this championship game?

531 Who did the hat-trick for Surrey at Leicester?

532 In the Middlesex first innings at Lord's which of the home players scored his first 50 since 1968?

533 Which slow bowler took 6-22 in the Surrey second innings?

534 Which two Surrey players retired at the end of season 1974?

535 Which Surrey player was suspended for two matches by the Test and County Cricket Board for dissenting from an umpire's decision?

MORE OF 1974

536 Who scored a century for Gloucestershire against his former county at The Oval in July?

537 Who took 10-72 for Surrey in The Oval match against Somerset in August?

538 Who carried his bat in the Sussex first innings at Hove in June?

539 Who got his first century against Surrey in the match at Bradford?

540 Who was the Yorkshire spinner who took 9-54 in this match?

541 Who scored a century against Kent in the Benson and Hedges match at Canterbury?

542 Surrey won this competition, their first one-day success. Which county did they defeat in the final?

543 Who was made Man of the Match?

544 Which bowler in the match had figures of 7-2-10-4?

545 Who took 6-25 in the John Player match v. Derbyshire at The Oval?

1973 TOURISTS AND COUNTIES

546 Which Surrey player scored the opening first-class century of the season against the Australians at The Oval in May?

547 Which of the tourists scored a century?

548 What was remarkable about the first Australian innings in the final Test at The Oval?

549 Which Kent batsman scored a century in each innings v. Surrey in the match at Maidstone in May?

550 Who, as opener, scored a century against Lancashire at Old Trafford in May?

551 Who was the Leicestershire opening bat who at Leicester took 4-6 to win the match there in June?

552 Which Northants batsmen made 234 for the third wicket at Northampton?

553 Which Somerset player had a match analysis of 9-89 in his side's innings win at The Oval in June?

554 Who scored a century for Cambridge against Surrey at Fenners?

555 Who were the three left-handed batsmen who scored a century in the Middlesex match at The Oval in July?

MORE OF 1973

556 Who hit his first championship century against Derbyshire at The Oval?

557 Which county did Surrey defeat by exactly the same margin as the previous season?

558 In this match which Surrey bowler had a hat-trick in the course of taking 12-58?

559 Which Glamorgan player got a double century at The Oval in August?

560 What other Test player got a century in this match for the Taffs?

561 What was truly noteworthy about Pat Pocock's last over against Sussex at Eastbourne?

562 How many run outs were there in the Essex innings at Harlow in the J. P. L. match against Surrey?

563 Who were the two West Indians with an age gap of 20 years who each scored 50's in the J. P. L. match v. Surrey at Southampton in July?

564 Who scored 96* in his benefit J. P. L. match against Surrey at Trent Bridge but nevertheless lost?

565 Who took 5-15 for Sussex in the J. P. L. match at Hove?

STILL MORE 1973

566 Who scored a century against Durham in the Gillette Cup at Chester-le-Street?

567 Whose analysis in the Surrey-Worcestershire second round match was an almost incredible 12-7-7-4?

568 Even more incredibly, he was not Man of that Match. Who was?

569 Who was the Surrey batsman who scored a century against the touring New Zealanders at The Oval in July?

570 In this match Glenn Turner scored 121*. What highly unusual distinction had he gained earlier in the season?

571 Which two players put on 155 at Cardiff for the ninth wicket against Glamorgan?

572 What was significant about Colin Cowdrey's century against Surrey at Maidstone in July?

573 Who made his top score in the Surrey first innings of that game?

574 Geoff Howarth's brother also played for New Zealand. His name?

575 Who finished the season third top of the national bowling averages and third top of the Surrey batting averages?

1973 BUSY OLD YEAR

576 Name the three Pakistani batsmen who made centuries in the match between Surrey and Gloucestershire at The Oval in May?

577 Which county, dismissed for 60 and 43 at The Oval, recorded their lowest aggregate in a three-day match for 108 years?

578 In this game whose match analysis was 9.3-4-11-7?

579 At Guildford which Northants batsman scored his first 50 since returning to the game after sustaining a serious non cricketing injury?

580 Who, batting at number nine, got a century against Sussex?

581 Who got the hat-trick against Yorkshire at Leeds?

582 Who set up a record first-wicket partnership for the Benson and Hedges competition against Essex at Chelmsford?

583 In the Kent match in that competition at The Oval, which visiting bowler took 5-21?

584 Which John Player League match ended in a tie?

585 Unusually for a Sunday match a player from each side scored a century. Identify the two players.

586 Where was Robin Jackman born?
587 From which part of the West Indies was he debarred?
588 What are his first names?
589 In which edition of Wisden was he Cricketer of the Year?
590 How many first-class wickets did he take in 1980?
591 How many of those were championship wickets?
592 He had an uncle who was a well-known actor. Who?
593 What record did he establish when at St Edmund's School Canterbury in 1962?
594 When did he join Surrey?
595 When was he capped?

THE 1979 SEASON

596 Which bowler had a career-best of 9-57 against Glamorgan at Cardiff?
597 Who hit the season's fastest century against Surrey at Cheltenham?
598 Who took 5-54 in that second Gloucestershire innings?
599 Surrey won by one wicket off the final ball. What happened?
600 Which Surrey bowler took 13-122 v. Hampshire at Portsmouth?
601 Which two Surrey openers scored hundreds in the match with Notts at Trent Bridge?
602 Which Surrey player in the Middlesex match at The Oval scored 82 and in the match took 8-99?
603 Who was the Middlesex bowler who saved the game by making 91*?
604 Who scored 200 for once out against Hampshire at The Oval?
605 In which match did a former Surrey player refuse to allow a current Surrey player to return to the field after illness?

FURTHER EVENTS OF 1979

606 Who scored his maiden century for Surrey against his old county?

607 Who was the ex-Surrey player who scored a century for Worcestershire in the county match at Guildford?

608 In that same match an ex-Surrey bowler took 8-94 for Worcester. Who was he?

609 Who were the three ex-Surrey players in the victorious Sussex side in the county match at Hove?

610 Who scored a century against Surrey for Worcester in both one-day and three-day competition?

611 Who beat Surrey in the final of the Benson and Hedges Cup and what was the margin?

612 Who scored a century in this Lord's final?

613 Who were the two Pakistan Test players who put on 105 for the first wicket for Gloucestershire in the J. P. L. match at Cheltenham?

614 In which J. P. L. match did rain rescue Surrey from a hopeless position because the opposition had only batted 9.4 overs?

615 A quick look forward to 1980: what did the years 1956 and 1980 have in common for Surrey?

SEASON 1977

616 Bob Willis was made Cricketer of the Year for his exploits in 1977. When and why did he leave Surrey?

617 When did he first appear for the county?

618 Who were the chief Surrey pace bowlers at the time?

619 Who scored a century against the touring Australians of 1977?

620 Graham Roope was the partner in the two great batting feats of the season. What were they?

621 Name the Essex player who scored 103 and 88 and the Surrey player who scored 115 and 79 in the match at Chelmsford?

622 Who at Cardiff in July 1977 established a record opening partnership against Glamorgan of 212?

623 Which two Hampshire batsmen scored centuries against Surrey at Bournemouth in the first innings in June 1977?

624 Which county match ended with 12 consecutive maiden overs?

625 Who saved Surrey at Trent Bridge with his fifth century of the season?

626 Who were the two Somerset batsmen who had a record partnership for the fourth wicket for the county against Surrey at Weston-super-Mare?

627 Who was the Surrey player who scored a century in this match?

628 John Edrich scored his 100th century. How many players had previously reached this landmark?

629 How many of them had been Surrey players?

630 Which Leicestershire player had a hat-trick in their win at The Oval?

631 Who was the Leicestershire player, later an umpire, who took 9-94 in that particular match?

632 Who, having made 264 for once out, was on the losing side to Surrey in one of the Guildford matches?

633 Who hit 56 from 32 balls to win the game against Warwickshire at The Oval?

634 Which former colleague did he hit for two sixes?

635 Who was the former Northants bowler who took 10-125 for Lancashire in the match at Old Trafford?

636 Which Surrey captain's son made his debut against Pakistan at The Oval in June 1978?

637 Who was the Derbyshire occasional bowler who at Ilkeston took 10-82 in the match, having previously only taken 19 wickets in his career?

638 Who set a Hampshire record with 14 consecutive maiden overs at Portsmouth?

639 Who was the Kent spinner who took 9-50 in the match against Surrey at Tunbridge Wells?

640 Surrey finished in their lowest position since World War II. What?

641 What ex-Surrey cricketer took 100 wickets for the first time in his career in the match against Surrey at The Oval?

642 Which two Surrey batsmen scored their maiden centuries in this year?

643 Who took 20 wickets against Surrey in two county matches?

644 He had an outstanding analysis against Surrey at The Oval. What was it?

645 Who was the Kent Test player who was awarded his county cap in the course of this match?

MORE 1978s

646 Who took part in the partnership of 211 for the third wicket against Glamorgan in August?

647 One of these batsmen had another century in the next home game with Lancashire as opponents. Which one?

648 Whose first three wickets in first-class county cricket came in the form of a hat-trick against Surrey?

649 Who were the Worcester pair who made 254 for the first wicket?

650 Who was the Cambridge University captain who scored a century in each innings against Surrey at Fenner's?

651 Who was the last University player to have achieved this against any of the counties?

652 In the Benson and Hedges competition Surrey beat Yorkshire by one wicket. Where in Yorkshire was this match played?

653 Which two bowlers bowled their 16 overs for 36 runs in the John Player League match against Essex?

654 The same two did even better at Tring against Northants. How much did their 16 overs cost on that occasion?

655 Despite this, Surrey lost to a hurricane century from whom?

THE LATE 1970s

656 Who were the Australian and Pakistan Test players and the namesake of the Sri Lanka captain in the Sussex side v. Surrey at Hove in June 1977?

657 In 1977 who was the umpire who operated at the bowler's end throughout the whole of the match against Oxford University and why?

658 Who scored 117 against Surrey, his former and future county, in the Benson and Hedges competition?

659 Who in his only over of the J. P. L. match v. Derbyshire, the last of the match, went for 14 runs thus losing the game?

660 Who scored his first John Player century against Surrey at Southampton? Clue: he would subsequently play for Surrey.

661 Who were the Leicester pair who in the Sunday game at Grace Road put on 140 for the second wicket?

662 As well as The Oval and Guildford what other Sunday venue did Surrey use in 1977?

663 Who was the Notts opener from Nairobi who scored his first J. P. L. century at The Oval in September 1977?

664 In which J. P. L. match at The Oval in 1977 were the opposition 0-4 and then 4-6?

665 What was odd about the score card?

PAT POCOCK

666 What nationality is Pat Pocock?

667 What is his nickname?

668 When he was recalled to the Test side in 1984 how long was it since he had played international cricket at top level?

669 Did he ever score a first-class century?

670 Did he ever take ten wickets in an innings?

671 Which Test country did he not tour?

672 What astonishing records did he set bowling against Sussex at Eastbourne in 1972?

673 When was he awarded his Surrey cap?

674 How often did he take ten wickets in a match?

675 What is his connection with W. G. Grace?

MOSTLY YOUNIS AHMED

676 Who in 1985 joined the county he'd taken 5-13 against at The Oval in 1983?

677 Who became captain of Surrey in his 23rd year with the county?

678 Who in the 1980s took a return ticket to Worcestershire?

679 For which three counties did Younis Ahmed play?

680 What was the name of his brother who played for Pakistan?

681 Did Younis himself play Test cricket?
682 How old was he when he made his first-class debut?
683 When did he make his debut for Surrey?
684 How many first-class hundreds has he scored?
685 What were his best bowling figures?

THE·YEAR 1980

686 Which two players of the touring Australian side had played in Scotland?
687 Who was the Essex spinner who took 11-118 against Surrey at Chelmsford?
688 Who had a career-best bowling performance for Surrey in the Lancashire first innings at Old Trafford?
689 In the Middlesex match at Lord's who put on 248 for the home side's fourth wicket?
690 Who scored 49 v. Northants and took 4-9 in their first innings?
691 Who took 5-28 at The Oval against his former county, Sussex?
692 Who did the hat-trick against Notts at The Oval in June?
693 Which two bowlers bowled unchanged in the second innings of the Essex match at The Oval in June?
694 What record did R. D. Jackman complete in the match against Gloucestershire at Guildford?
695 Who scored a double century against Cambridge University at Fenners?

MORE OF 1980

696 In the 1980 match at Fenners who put on 266 for the first wicket for Surrey with Alan Butcher?
697 In which one-day match did Sylvester Clarke bowl 12-7-9-1?
698 In which Gillette Cup match did Surrey win with the scores tied?
699 Who took 5-22 for Surrey in this match?
700 How many extras were there in the Yorkshire semi-final total of 135?
701 Who was the Man of the Match in the Gillette Cup final with Middlesex?

702 Who was the ex-Surrey bowler who in this match returned figures of 12-5-17-2?

703 Another Middlesex bowler had the even more remarkable figures of 11-5-13-0 against Surrey in the Benson and Hedges Cup. Who was he?

704 In the same competition who took 5-23 for Surrey against Kent?

705 Who scored 109 for Hampshire out of their total of 193-9 in the Benson and Hedges Cup?

THE YEAR 1981

706 Who took 10-72 for Gloucestershire in the Surrey match during the Cheltenham Festival?

707 In which match did Robin Jackman take four wickets for no runs in the space of eight balls?

708 Who hit 79 in 45 minutes against Lancashire at Old Trafford?

709 Who took 10-171 in the match with Middlesex at Lord's? The bowler was a Middlesex player.

710 Who had match figures of 9 94 against Surrey at Trent Bridge?

711 Who retired at the end of the 1981 season?

712 Where had he been before joining Surrey?

713 Who made 116 at The Oval for Worcestershire against his former county?

714 Who scored his maiden championship century against Leicestershire at The Oval?

715 Who was the Kent bowler who returned a highly creditable 12-147 against Surrey at The Oval?

THE 1982 SEASON

716 In the match at Derby who was the first player in 17 years to hit two centuries for them in a match?

717 Who took seven wickets for Surrey in the Old Trafford match and scored 134*?

718 In the course of his innings he had a partnership of 172 which

was only one short of the Surrey last-wicket record. Who assisted him?

719 What were his figures in the next match?

720 Who arrived at Lord's as a sub-postmaster and ended up playing?

721 What was his contribution?

722 How old was he and how long was it since he made his first-class debut?

723 Who had a match analysis of 10-109 for Surrey at Northampton?

724 Who left the county in 1982? Clue: he played for England.

725 Who had a personal best bowling analysis when Surrey were dismissed for 101 in their second innings against Hampshire?

THE YEAR 1983

726 What was remarkable about the Surrey first innings against Essex at Chelmsford in May 1983?

727 Who bowled unchanged throughout the innings?

728 Who scored a century for Surrey in the second innings?

729 Which two players scored centuries in the Surrey second innings against Glamorgan at Swansea?

730 Who scored 218 for once out for Somerset against Surrey at Taunton?

731 Who was the Somerset player who in this match scored 41 and 48 and took 8-209?

732 Which Lancashire player had a king pair in the match at The Oval?

733 Who, in June, hit his maiden century against Oxford University at The Oval?

734 For what other reason was this match memorable for him?

735 Who conceded 17 byes out of 32 extras in the Gloucestershire match at The Oval?

THE YEAR 1984

736 In which match were Surrey's tactics branded "a disgrace" by the opposition captain?

737 Who were the opposing captains in this match?

738 Roger Knight made his best score for eight years against one of his former counties. What was it and where did he make it?

739 Which Australian bowler had match figures of 8-87 against Surrey at Canterbury?

740 In which match did two opposing off-spinners each take ten wickets?

741 Who scored 70 for Surrey in the first innings of the Middlesex match at Lord's and also took nine wickets?

742 Who was the Scot who took 8-96 in the match between Surrey and Notts at Trent Bridge in June 1984?

743 Which prominent Surrey player retired from first-class cricket?

744 He had hit a century against every county bar one. Which?

745 Who, after 13 years in first-class cricket, hit two centuries in the match against Glamorgan at The Oval?

RECENT EVENTS

746 Who was the Scot who hit eight 50s in 11 championship games for Surrey in 1982?

747 Who took 11-111 against the county champions Essex at The Oval that year?

748 Also that season, who scored his maiden century against Nottinghamshire?

749 And who in 1982 took 5-13 in nine overs against Gloucestershire?

750 Who in 1984 dismissed the first three Surrey batsmen at Guildford and then hit a century for Sussex?

751 Who carried his bat in the first innings of the Derbyshire match at The Oval?

752 Who, in the same season, got a century against Kent starting as night watchman?

753 In 1984 Surrey had their best-ever opening stand against Yorkshire. Who were the batsmen concerned?

754 Was this a record for a Surrey home game?

755 Who were the Surrey debutants who against Cambridge University put on 189 for the eighth wicket after Surrey had been 172-7?

756 Who hit 140 against India in the one-day match at The Oval?

757 Who captained the side in his last year as a player?

758 On which ground did he visit the pressbox to say that the pitch was a disgrace?

759 Who scored 101 runs, 27 and 74 for Gloucestershire in a low-scoring match at Bristol and then took 4-60 in Surrey's second innings?

760 Who said of his own side "I have never before seen any side beaten by an innings on such a good cricket wicket"?

761 In the match against Middlesex at Uxbridge who were the two young players who scored a century and took ten wickets respectively?

762 Who took 10-172 for Nottinghamshire at Trent Bridge?

763 Who missed a century by one run on his first appearance as a Surrey player at The Oval?

764 Who was the Surrey bowler who, coming into the side as a replacement, took 12-113 against Warwickshire at The Oval in May?

765 He had fine second innings figures of 7-23. Against which county?

IN AND OUT

766 What do John Emburey, Mike Selvey and Bob Willis have in common?

767 Has Nick Falkner ever scored a century?

768 Who was the 1985 big name signing, who left in 1987?

769 From which county had he come?

770 He scored over 20,000 runs in county cricket. How long did it take before he made his first century?

771 Which Surrey batsman has recorded a pair before lunch at Lord's?

772 Why is Roger Knight uneasy when Monte Lynch is batting?

773 Monte Lynch has recorded his fastest century and best bowling against the same county. Which one?

774 Who was the Whitechapel boy who made a century on his debut in 1984?

775 Where was this game played?

ENEMY DEEDS

776 Who was the Middlesex pace bowler who hit 66 against Surrey at Lord's in 1984?

777 Who scored 159 for Kent at Canterbury in 1985?

778 Who is the Hampshire Test batsman whose best bowling performance is five in an innings against Surrey?

779 What Sydney University coach took 7-35 for Middlesex at The Oval in 1986?

780 The youngest-ever cricketer to play for Yorkshire took 7-55 against Surrey at Headingley in 1986. Who was he?

781 Who is the South African-born bowler whose best batting performance was a century against Surrey at Guildford in 1984?

782 Who is the cricketer, still playing, who scored 181* for Hampshire at The Oval in 1969?

783 One for Surrey this time: who scored 143 on his debut at Derby in 1985?

784 Who is the player, who beginning with Cheshire, scored 106 for Lancs at Southport in 1985?

785 Who scored his maiden county century against Surrey at Cheltenham in 1984?

PACEMAN AND KEEPER

786 From which part of the West Indies does Tony Gray hail?

787 In which county match of 1985 did he perform the hat-trick?

788 In that match he also recorded his best bowling performance to date. What was it?

789 Jack Richards is a Cornishman. Can you name two other Cornishmen who have figured in first-class cricket?

790 His first championship century was 117* against which county?

791 How many first-class wickets has he taken?

792 Who was his England rival who recorded his best-ever batting performance against Surrey at The Oval in 1986?

793 Who was the other wicket-keeper in the last tour of Australia when Richards was selected?

794 On what ground did he make his century in a Test?

795 Who was the Surrey wicket-keeper who had his England cap before he was awarded his county cap?

EIGHTIES ROUND UP

796 In 1982 who scored 168 for once out for Notts at The Oval?

797 In that year what Surrey player scored a direct hit on another's car at Guildford?

798 What else did both men have in common in that match?

799 Who was the South African player who reached a century for Glamorgan in this match?

800 In 1986 who was the Australian who saved the match for Essex with a century?

801 What remarkable occurrence was there in the 1986 match against Gloucestershire at The Oval in September involving a wicket-keeper?

802 Had this ever occurred before?

803 It was altogether a good match for wicket-keepers. Why?

804 Which Surrey player, as last man, appealed against the light to save the match against Worcestershire?

805 Who carried his bat in the second innings of the match against Yorkshire at Leeds?

CURRENT AND RECENT PERFORMERS

806 Besides Micky and Alex, there is a third Stewart connected with cricket. Who is he?

807 Who was the recent Surrey player who by the age of 24 had played for three counties?

Which Surrey players answer to the following nicknames:

808 Spandau?

809 Pipsqueak?

810 Vulture?

811 Teddy?

812 Which batting distinction did Sylvester Clarke achieve in the 1981 season?

813 What in early days was his preferred fielding position?

814 Who was responsible for Sylvester Clarke coming to The Oval?

815 Against which county did he perform the hat-trick in 1980?

THE 1986 SEASON

816 Which Surrey player made four successive ducks in the month of June?

817 Who was the reserve Surrey wicket-keeper in 1986?

818 Who moved to Glamorgan at the end of the season?

819 What record had he set against Glamorgan in 1980?

820 For which county did his brother play?

821 Who left at the end of the 1986 season to go back to the soil?

822 How many first-class centuries had he made?

823 Who at the end of the 1986 season had made only 2620 runs in ten seasons but had hit four centuries?

824 Who was the Surrey Scot who went off to Wales?

825 Name the two sons of former captains who have played for Surrey in the last ten years?

INDIVIDUAL HAPPENINGS

826 Who was the Surrey all-rounder, formerly an amateur, who retired at the end of the 1966 season?

827 How much did Tony Lock's benefit raise?

828 Why did Bernard Constable miss much of the 1960 season?

829 Against whom did John Edrich score his 100th century?

830 How many first-class innings had he played by that time?

831 When had he scored his first county century?

832 How many centuries did he score against Australia?

833 Who was the first Surrey captain after World War II?

834 He was followed by E. R. T. Holmes again, then by whom?

835 Who was the Surrey player who died suddenly in the close season of 1949-1950?

836 Who was the amateur who in his only three appearances for Surrey made 107* against Northants on his debut at Northampton in 1921, then scored 9 and 53* and never played again, all this in 1921?

837 How many centuries did R. J. Gregory score?

838 How many times did he score 1000 runs in a season?

839 And how many times 2000 runs in a season?

840 He was an all-rounder. How many wickets and catches had he?

841 Who was the Hampshire all-rounder who scored a century in each innings v. Surrey at The Oval in 1927 in the match where Hobbs did likewise?

842 Who was the well-known music-hall artiste who played for Surrey during the 1920s?

843 In 1927 he figured in a partnership of 119 in 65 minutes against Essex. Who was at the other end?

844 How did the variety star mark his first spell as a bowler in county cricket?

845 How many centuries did Lord Dalmeny score for Surrey?

REALLY MIXED GRILL

846 Who was the Yorkshire born Glamorgan bat who had his highest ever score, 205, against Surrey at The Oval in 1932?

847 Who was the Sussex captain who became Treasurer and Vice-President of Surrey and Peter May's father-in-law?

848 Who was the Sudanese civil servant on long leave who with S. Lee put on 208 for the first wicket at Lord's to win the championship for Middlesex in 1920 against Surrey?

849 Name the Cambridge Blue who made 117 against Leicestershire in 1931 and put on 199 with Andrew Sandham?

850 Who had the only five wicket haul for Surrey in the 1978 J.P.L.?

851 When Worcester bowled Surrey out for 64 in the J.P.L. match of July 1978 which of their bowlers had his best one-day return?

852 Who was the Derbyshire bat who, when making 74 at The Oval in 1950, recorded the highest score ever on debut for that county?

853 Who was the army major who took 7-42 for Warwickshire at The Oval in 1930?

854 Who played the first-ever innings of over 300 for Notts in the 1939 match against Middlesex at The Oval?

855 Why on earth was a Middlesex-Notts match played at The Oval?

SURREY NICKNAMES

Who, over the ages, have answered to the following nicknames:

856 Silver Billy?
857 The Gu'vnor?
858 The Master?
859 Andy Sandy?
860 The Lobster?
861 Razor?
862 Horse?
863 The Colonel?
864 Felix?
865 Shrimp?

CURIOSITIES

866 Name the Warwickshire bowler who in 1928 at Edgbaston dismissed the first seven Surrey batsmen in taking 8-62?

867 Can you name his victims, or most of them?

868 Who was the Cambridge Blue of 1949 who appeared for Surrey in 1950 and 1951 as a fast medium bowler?

869 Who was the Arsenal chairman who with Aidan Crawley put on 153 against Surrey for Oxford University at The Oval in 1928?

870 Who was the teenage Warwickshire pace bowler who took 5-29 against Surrey at Edgbaston in June 1980?

871 What was the double significance of Younis Ahmed's 56 against Surrey in the J.P.L. at Worcester in July 1980?

872 Who was the secretary of Surrey who was also secretary of Essex?

873 When "Bosser" Martin retired as head groundsman in 1940 how long had he been at The Oval?

874 What was odd about the dismissal of J. Herbert King of Leicestershire in May 1906?

875 In the 1981 match against Cambridge University at Fenners which student took 4-39 in Surrey's first innings and then made 55* in the Cambridge second innings?

ODDS AND ENDS

876 Who was the Irishman who turned out regularly for Surrey in the mid-1930s, fielded as substitute against Australia at The Oval in 1934 and played football for Millwall Athletic?

877 Who was the President of MCC who wrote *The History of Cricket* and played six times for Surrey in 1912?

878 Who was the American who playing against Surrey in 1903 scored 98 and 113* and took six wickets?

879 The Attorney-General of Edward VIII became President of Surrey. Who was he?

880 Who played twice for Surrey in 1911 and became a regular for Somerset 11 years later?

881 Which Cambridge University player topped the Surrey bowling averages in 1903?

882 Who, in his one game for Surrey, bowled W. G. Grace twice?

883 What world record was set in 1964 in the match against Sussex at Hove?

884 H. C. McDonnell's best-ever bowling performance was 15-138. Against whom?

885 Who was the Middlesex player whose use of bad language in 1897 caused Surrey to refuse to play against him?

MIXED BAG

886 Name two Surrey players who captained Northamptonshire and played for England?

887 In Surrey history who were the famous "Four H's"?

888 What particularly distinguished the appearance of Bill Hitch on the field?

889 Who was the masseur who looked after Surrey players from 1929-65?
890 Which Surrey bowler performed a Test hat-trick for England in 1957?
891 What was unusual about the 1967 county cricket season for Surrey?
892 Who was the famous groundsman who was in charge at The Oval from 1945-67?
893 When did Younis Ahmed become a first eleven player?
894 Who was the Surrey fast bowler who missed the whole of 1966 through injury?
895 Which Surrey cricketer has done the double for more than one county?

GENERAL POST

896 When did play first take place at The Oval?
897 Who is the club's landlord?
898 Who was the Surrey bowler who in pre-World War I days took 112 wickets in 18 Tests at an average of 10.75?
899 What happened to him?
900 Which Surrey quick bowler took 1179 wickets in the course of five English seasons?
901 Which Surrey player took nine wickets and scored a century against the Gentlemen in the match of 1902?
902 Between 1872 and 1896 Surrey and the Football Association had the same Secretary. Who was he?
903 What was the first overseas team to play at The Oval?
904 When was the first Test played there?
905 Who are the four Surrey players who have scored a 100 centuries?

MOSTLY BOWLERS

906 Who was the fast bowler from Dulwich who, as a Surrey player took 12-183 against the Players at Lord's in 1906?
907 Why was slow bowler W. C. Smith known as "Razor" Smith?

908 Who took all ten Somerset wickets in an innings at Taunton in 1921?

909 Who were the two bowlers who bowled unchanged in dismissing Yorkshire for 26 at The Oval in 1909?

910 Who was the brother of J. N. Crawford who also played for Surrey?

911 What Surrey player besides Herbert Strudwick had a 60-year connection with the club?

912 Who became captain of Surrey in 1952?

913 How long was he captain and how many county championships did his sides win?

914 He never played for England. What other honour eluded him?

915 When Surrey beat the 1956 Australians it was the first victory by a county over them since when?

HERE AND THERE

916 In 1956 who took all ten Australian wickets in the first innings?

917 Who scored a century for Surrey in the same match?

918 How did Ian Johnson, the Australian captain, mark the Surrey victory?

919 Who was known as The Surrey Poet?

920 In 1963 Surrey used four wicket-keepers. Name them?

921 Who was the gifted Surrey amateur batsman of the 1920s who was dropped after it was pointed out that he had been born on the Kent side of the road where he lived?

922 How many centuries had he scored and how many appearances for the Gentlemen did he make?

923 Who took four wickets in four balls against Sussex at The Oval in 1924?

924 Who were the Surrey bowlers who bowled unchanged throughout the match with Sussex in 1907?

925 One of these bowlers actually performed this unusual feat twice. Who was he and what was the other occasion?

ODDITIES

926 What was the name of the amateur bowler who was capped in 1920?

927 Which Marshal of the RAF was President of Surrey?

928 Which Australian cricketer hit a career-best (at that time) 240 against Surrey at the Oval in 1934?

929 Who holds the record first wicket partnership for Surrey?

930 What was the summer of Edward James Sheffield?

931 Who was the batsman who for Middlesex against Surrey in 1903 made 89 and 118 at Lord's and 112 at The Oval?

932 What was noteworthy about Laurie Fishlock's 100 against Warwickshire at The Oval in 1935?

933 Who was wrongly given out in the match with Cambridge at The Oval in 1924?

934 What was the only tune Laurie Fishlock could play on his banjo?

935 Who came to The Oval from Kent in 1979?

FINAL LOOK ROUND

936 Why were The Oval flags at half-mast during the first championship match of 1986 against Nottinghamshire?

937 In the 1986 season three Surrey bowlers were in the first ten of the national averages. Sylvester Clarke and Tony Gray were two. The third was?

938 Which Surrey player was suspended in 1986 for disciplinary reasons?

939 Who in 1986 scored a double century and 179 but failed to score 1000 first-class runs?

940 Are friendly matches between full strength county sides considered to be first-class fixtures?

941 Why were Surrey very grateful to Alan Walker of Northamptonshire at the end of the 1986 season?

942 When did Micky Stewart become team manager of Surrey?

943 Who at the end of 1986 said "P.P. does not stand for Peter Pan"?

944 Richard Hadlee was Man of the Match although on the losing side in the 1986 Nat. West quarter-final. What was his performance?

945 Who was the New Zealand Test player who scored a century for Worcestershire in the first innings of their match at The Oval on 8 August?

946 Powerful man about to hit powerfully. Who is he?

947 Skipper and man of three counties. Identify him?

948 Batsman, bowler and gully fielder. Who is this left-hander?

949 The captain takes the field at The Oval. Which captain?

950 Another captain and one of the very greatest. Name him.

951 Half a dozen greats on The Oval balcony during the 1981 Centenary celebrations of Test cricket there. Who are these redoubtable six men?

952 Old England v. Old Australia, The Oval 1980. Who are the captains?

953 This back foot player has something in common with Sir Jack
Hobbs. What?

954 How many Surrey players in this Old England XI of 1980?

955 Who are these two Surrey stalwarts of the 1970s?

956 Pace bowler, played with Sussex and England also, became county coach. Who is he?

957 "It's been a hard day's night." Two Surrey fielders would subscribe to that. Can you name them?

958 Another Surrey captain. Clue — he lost form so badly that he had to leave himself out of the county side.

959 Who is thanking the actors who helped in the Ken Barrington Appeal?

960 A non-cricket question. Can you identify the actors?

961 One of the longest-serving players Surrey have ever had, certainly their longest-serving Welshman. Who?

962 At least he started out with Surrey. Where did he go?

963 "Just like Dad used to do!" Who is this member of the present staff?

964 Dependable opener, great battler, most valuable import. Who?

965 Elegant left-hander on his way to his best-ever score for Surrey. Who, where and how many?

966 Who are the two Surrey fielders in this incident from the
England v. India Test match at Old Trafford in 1959?

967 The umpire at the bowler's end, who is he?

968 The bowler is fairly obvious but who is the Surrey batsman?

969 A let-off for Ken Barrington in the slips. Against whom?

970 "Good day to you, sir!" The look of a 'keeper who knows that he has beaten the downthrust bat. The cap is the clue to the 'keeper.

971 He followed in an earlier Surrey player's footsteps and went off
to captain the same county. England player and left-hand bat,
who is he?

972 Who is the Indian wicket-keeper in this photograph?

973 Answers to "The Big Man" but his Sunday name is?

974 Chesterfield supporter, racing enthusiast and scorer of centuries in the lower middle order. Who is this useful chap?

975 He's played in Antigua, Dubai and Australia and is a left-
armer. Who?

976 There are two Surrey captains (in the middle of the back and centre rows) in this team of 1887. Can you identify them?

977 This is the 1914 team, the captain is centre front row. Skipper is?

978 Gifted fast bowler who died quite young in South Africa. He is?

979 Another greatheart who regarded anything under 200 wickets as a poor season. Had a brief spell with Somerset so he is therefore?

980 Surrey's highest ever total, with the 357 belonging to?

981 He set a record for a season's aggregate that would last until
Dennis Compton took it from him in 1947. Precursor of
Hobbs.

982 Opening pair, 1914. Too easy, really!

983 And opening pair around 1939?

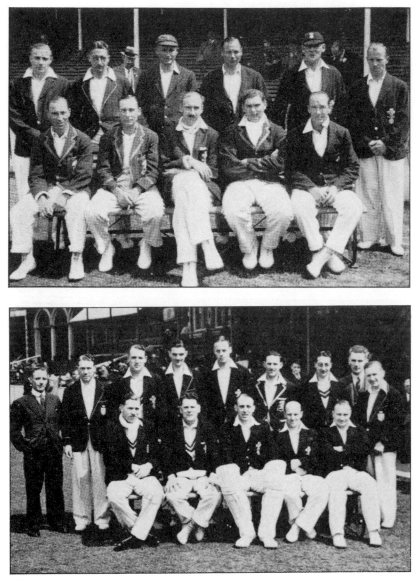

984 Surrey sides of 1929 and 1939. Who are the four players
common to both groups?

985 Who is the captain, front row centre, in the lower picture?

986 In the 1929 picture who is the amateur seated second right in
the front row?

987 Hasn't kept it down has he? Which batsman may be out caught?

988 Admired and feared, rather than loved. The cap is the give-away.

989 He spanned the wars as a batsman-skipper.

990 Tearaway slinger and motivator par excellence.

991 "Like saplings in a hurricane!" Who were on the receiving end
of this titanic piece of bowling from Eddie Watts in 1937?

992 Can you identify this pace bowler of the 1930s and 1940s?

993 The embodiment of pugnacity and 25 years at the top. Who?

994 Rocking motion in delivery. But which one?

995 Tiptoeing upon the first-class scene. The shy youth?

996 The player presenting the trophy will later play in the same
Surrey side as the youngster receiving it. Who are they?

997 Who is presenting this ball to Jim Laker?
998 More importantly, why?
999 Even more unbelievably, what happened later?

1000 His Majesty George VI at The Oval in 1939. Who is making
the introductions?

1001 Her Majesty Queen Elizabeth also came to The Oval in 1955.
Who are the first three players in the Surrey line-up?

1002 Here are three Surrey catchers from the great days of the
1950s. Who are the successful fielders?

1003 Back-room boys are equally important to the success of a county club. Who was this well-known secretary?

1004 This keeper and keeper of the score?

1005 This soother of aches and pains?

1006 How many England players in this Surrey group of 1956?

1007 Well done! Who is congratulating who here?

1008 Who is the young bowler about to let go?

1009 Surrey v. Leicestershire 1952. Who is the Oval favourite at the crease?

1010 And the Leicestershire keeper?

1011 Who scored first double century for 20 years for Surrey at The Oval in 1987 but didn't stay long?

1012 Unusual spectacle at The Oval. What was the sport and who
are the teams?

1013 Trevor Jesty receives the Honeywell Award. Why, and who is with him?

Answers

1 Stanley Christopherson who was MCC president from 1939-46.
2 W. E. Roller.
3 In the Long Room at The Oval there is a massive picture of him going out to bat.
4 H. D. Leveson-Gower.
5 E. Pooley who was acquitted at Christchurch.
6 He had 12 victims behind the wicket in a match against Sussex. Eight were caught and four stumped
7 "J. Southerton, retired, thinking he was out, caught." He refused to carry on even although given not out and asked to remain.
8 Edward Barratt.
9 W. E. Roller in the circumstances mentioned above.
10 John Beamont.

MORE EARLY DAYS

11 Nottinghamshire.
12 He carried his bat through both completed innings. As late as 1956 there had only been three other cases of this.
13 Maurice Read against Australia at The Oval in 1893.
14 Yes, in his last season, his second dismissal being a run-out!
15 Yes. Essex were not yet in the county championship but had been given first-class status in April 1894.
16 K. J. Key and W. S. Surridge.
17 W. Howell.
18 Bobby Abel.
19 Two matches were cancelled, against Sussex and Leicestershire.
20 Lord Dalmeny obtained permission for this to be done in 1905.

TOM HAYWARD

21 He was a groundsman at Parker's Piece in Cambridge.
22 Jack Hobbs.
23 He scored 1074 runs before the end of May.

24 He was 21 years at The Oval finishing up in 1914.
25 In 1897.
26 He hit four centuries in a week, 144* and 100 against Notts at Trent Bridge, 143 and 125 against Leicestershire at The Oval.
27 He had two hat-tricks, against Gloucestershire at The Oval and against Derbyshire at Chesterfield.
28 Twice, in 1904 and 1906.
29 His top score was 315 against Lancashire at The Oval in 1898.
30 Partnered by Bobby Abel who made 193, he himself made 273 in the match against Yorkshire at The Oval in 1899.

BEFORE THE KAISER

31 W. G. Quaife.
32 A. E. "Jim" Street. He scored 48 out of 97 all out in the tied Lancashire match of 1894 and then umpired the Somerset-Sussex match of 1919.
33 C. J. Kortright.
34 Charlie Chaplin.
35 Because of his fondness for underarm, or lob, bowling.
36 S. J. Storey in 1966.
37 G. A. Lohmann.
38 98.
39 G. Burton.
40 C. Aubrey Smith, well known at The Oval.

HITCH AND SMITH

41 "And worship a statue of Hitch." From a verse in *Punch*..
42 Glamorgan.
43 Todmorden.
44 Three, with his highest score being 107 against Somerset at Bath 1922.
45 Two tours, those of 1911-12 and 1920-21.
46 He made 51* in 40 minutes against a very strong tourist attack.
47 Smith and Rushby bowled unchanged in dismissing Yorkshire for 26, their lowest-ever score in 1905.

48 He took 247 wickets in 1910, 215 of them in championship games.

49 He took 14-29 in the match.

50 He worked with Surridge's the bat-makers, who were to provide a future Surrey captain in Stuart Surridge.

JACK HOBBS

51 At The Oval in 1905.

52 15.

53 D. R. Jardine.

54 Only once, in the shortened season of 1914.

55 Dr W. G. Grace.

56 111.

57 Essex.

58 12 in Test cricket.

59 Appendicitis.

60 Once, in 1925.

JACK HOBBS AGAIN

61 Three, one in 1914 which was spoiled by the war, one in 1919 and the last in 1926.

62 43 years of age.

63 316* against Middlesex at Lord's in August 1926.

64 He was the first professional English cricketer to be knighted.

65 Against Sussex. He only scored one century against them and his career average was a comparatively modest 34.64.

66 0, against Glamorgan at Cardiff in August 1934.

67 W. G. Grace.

68 107.

69 7-56 against Oxford University in 1911.

70 5-21 against Warwickshire at Edgbaston in 1920.

MORE ON SIR JACK

71 Only two first-class games. He was capped after his first county match against Essex in which he scored 155 runs.

72 Lord Dalmeny, Surrey captain, later Earl of Rosebery.
73 In 1925 when he overtook W. G. Grace's tally of hundreds.
74 16.
75 He made 266* the highest score since the fixture began in 1806.
76 Against Lancashire at Old Trafford in 1934.
77 George Duckworth's benefit match.
78 In the Strand.
79 Colin Cowdrey.
80 Quite true.

J. N. CRAWFORD

81 Repton.
82 Starting straight from Repton in August he topped the Surrey bowling averages with 44 wickets at 16.93.
83 Twice.
84 On twelve occasions.
85 30 wickets at 24.73 runs each.
86 In 1911 having gone to Australia following a disagreement with the county committee, he scored 110 for an Australian Eleven against the visiting Test side of that year.
87 Jack Hobbs.
88 Kent at The Oval in 1919.
89 78.
90 Bowler Tom Rushby.

P. G. H. FENDER

91 With Sussex. He moved to Surrey in 1914.
92 19,034 runs and 1894 wickets.
93 Six times.
94 Against Northamptonshire at Northampton in 1920. He reached his 100 in 35 minutes.
95 Six times.
96 He was joint captain with A. C. Wilkinson in 1920 and from 1921-31 he was in full charge of the side.
97 He was the first player to hold 50 catches in a season as well as performing the double.

98 The Gentlemen against the Players.

99 13.

100 In Australia 1920-21 with the modest return of 12 wickets at 34.

STRUDWICK AND SANDHAM

101 Mitcham.

102 60 years, 30 as stumper and 30 as scorer.

103 False. He had 1493 victims.

104 He played in 28 Tests.

105 He was made an honorary Life Member of MCC.

106 Andrew Sandham played with Surrey from 1911 to 1937.

107 He made 325 against the West Indies at Kingston in 1930. At the time this was regarded as a representative match but was later upgraded to Test status.

108 He made 219, the highest score by a county cricketer against an Australian touring team.

109 He made 107 centuries.

110 Against Sussex at Hove in September 1937.

THE ROARING TWENTIES

111 A. E. R. Gilligan.

112 R. H. Twining 135.

113 S. Fenley who took 73 wickets at an average of 19.

114 Oxford University.

115 Against Lancashire at Old Trafford, Surrey 567, Lancashire 588-4.

116 F. Watson 300*.

117 It was the highest-ever score made at Old Trafford.

118 Alf Gover.

119 M. J. C. Allom took 5-14 and A. C. T. Geary 5-22.

120 M. J. C. Allom took 67 wickets.

BETWEEN THE WARS (I)

121 He was a double international for England at cricket and soccer.

122 He died in 1942 while batting during a war-time match at Lord's.

123 On 20 occasions, two of them abroad.

124 He had 63 century partnerships with Jack Hobbs.

125 For 12 seasons, from 1920 to 31.

126 Against Northamptonshire at Northampton when he reached his century in 35 minutes.

127 Against Middlesex he took six wickets in 11 balls for one run. This record stood until surpassed by another Surrey bowler, Pat Pocock, against Sussex at Eastbourne in 1972.

128 D. R. Jardine, E. R. T. Holmes, H. M. Garland-Wells.

129 Alf Gover.

130 Alec and Eric Bedser.

BETWEEN THE WARS (2)

131 Naumann — F. C. G. played for Oxford and J. H. for Cambridge.

132 A. E. R. Gilligan for Cambridge and F. W. Gilligan for Oxford.

133 Captain Woolf Barnato, son of the famous Barney Barnato.

134 F. R. Brown who missed out with Northants in 1952.

135 F. R. Brown.

136 Middlesex. He scored 212 at The Oval and 135 at Lord's.

137 Only once, in 1948.

138 Against New Zealand in 1949.

139 "Bosser" Martin, the Surrey head groundsman, was called to Lord's to advise on a plague of leatherjackets which had stripped the square.

140 The Test match against West Indies in August 1939.

THE 1930s

141 Lloyd Budd.

142 E. M. Wellings.

143 Alf Gover.

144 Six Surrey players played in both matches, Gregory, Fishlock, Squires, Parker, Watts, Gover.

145 Harry Baldwin.

146 I. J. Siedle whose other centuries were against Oxford University and MCC.

147 E. A. Watts.

148 Yes, in 1938 he took 114 championship wickets at 17.69.

149 He was Alf Gover's brother-in-law.

150 Eight ball overs were tried but the idea was unpopular and was not revived after the war.

1938: AN AUSTRALIAN YEAR

151 Ben Barnett with 120*.

152 Maurice Leyland 187 and Joe Hardstaff Junior 169*.

153 L. O. Fleetwood-Smith.

154 Jack Fingleton (both innings) and Don Bradman.

155 H. M. Garland-Wells.

156 Harold Butler.

157 R. J. Gregory 243.

158 F. R. Brown.

159 It was the first county match to be played at Guildford.

160 Fishlock went to drive a no-ball, smashed a piece off his bat and the ball rebounded to the wicket-keeper, W. K. "Hopper" Levett, who broke the wicket with Fishlock out of his ground.

THE LATE 1930s

161 Alf Gover.

162 Score a century in each innings against Yorkshire.

163 D. J. Knight, also of Surrey, who curiously returned to the Surrey side in 1937 after an absence of ten years.

164 E. W. Whitfield, 77 and 174*.

165 L. L. Wilkinson.

166 Alf Gover.

167 Bill Bowes 6-32 and Frank Smailes 4-16.

168 Len Hutton.

169 M. M. Walford, later to play for Somerset.

170 41,284 runs at 44.83.

171 In the Wisden of 1946.

172 Dulwich Hamlet.

173 Crystal Palace.

174 Two, in 1936-37 and 1946-47.

175 He came to The Oval as a left-arm medium pace bowler.

176 In 1935 against Warwickshire at The Oval.

177 Against India in 1936.

178 He made three centuries against Yorkshire, two in the match at The Oval.

179 Bill Edrich of Middlesex and James Langridge of Sussex.

180 At an average of 50.

THE WAR AND JUST AFTER

181 It was a searchlight site first of all and then converted to a Prisoner of War camp although never used in that capacity.

182 Seven high explosive bombs and countless incendiaries were dropped on it.

183 21 August 1945.

184 Greyhound racing.

185 Sussex and Northants.

186 The Sussex match was played at New Malden and the one against Northants at Hastings.

187 Leicestershire.

188 The Royal Australian Air Force XI.

189 Alf Gover, E. R. T. Holmes and Laurie Fishlock.

190 Freddie Brown.

THE YEAR 1946

191 The Indian last pair, Sarwate and Banerjee, put on 249 in the first innings. Never before had numbers ten and eleven scored a century in the same innings of a match.

192 C. S. Nayudu had a hat-trick.

193 Alan Watkins with 119*.

194 Tom Goddard.

195 Jack Parker.

196 Leicestershire at Leicester, 129 and 112.

197 Against Lancashire at Old Trafford in June 1946.

198 W. J. Edrich, 147, and D. C. S. Compton, 235.

199 Northants, at Kettering.

200 Somerset at Weston-super-Mare.

MORE OF 1946

201 Five. Fishlock, Gover and Alec Bedser were on Test duty against India while McIntyre and Whittaker were injured.

202 Harold Gimblett of Somerset, 101 in May 1946.

203 Surrey v. Old England.

204 E. Brooks, the Surrey pre-war wicket-keeper.

205 Peter Smith.

206 A. V. Avery and T. G. Dodds.

207 Arthur McIntyre 127 and Whittaker 102.

208 Field Marshal Montgomery.

209 He was born at the local vicarage, St Mark's Kensington.

210 It was not scored in a championship match but in a friendly in aid of the Centenary Fund to rehabilitate The Oval.

PLAY RESUMES AFTER HITLER

211 1928-49.

212 In all first-class matches he scored just over 19,000 runs.

213 He made 37 centuries.

214 He ran the family's sports outfitters (specialising in cricket bats) and had a willow farm for their manufacture.

215 J. W. McMahon.

216 R. E. S. Wyatt.

217 A. Coxon 11-3-17-6 and Aspinall 11.5-1-23-3.

218 F. S. Trueman.

219 Jim Laker 11-123 for Surrey, Peter Robinson 11-119 for Somerset.

220 Peter May scored 124, his first century at The Oval, and Stuart Surridge took 7-80 in the Kent first innings, a personal best.

1947—THE SUNSHINE YEAR

221 Alan Melville who made 122.

222 Len Muncer.

223 Against Hampshire at Portsmouth.

224 He was on a hat-trick three times having three times taken two wickets in two balls.

225 Cyril Washbrook who made 251.

226 F. G. Mann of Middlesex, 106.

227 Surrey made a mammoth 706/4 declared.

228 Four, Fletcher 194, Squires 154, Parker 108* and Holmes 122*.

229 It was only his second championship match for Surrey.

230 A. V. Bedser, 126.

MORE SUNSHINE FROM 1947

231 Alf Gover.

232 Tom Goddard.

233 Tom Clark.

234 D. V. P. Wright.

235 Jack Parker, 204*.

236 Alec Bedser.

237 Bill Bowes.

238 Willie Watson, later of Leicestershire.

239 Guy Willatt.

240 D. C. S. Compton.

1948—THE DON'S FAREWELL

241 S. G. Barnes 176 and A. L. Hassett 110 in the Australian's 632 all out.

242 Laurie Fishlock with 81* out of a total of 141?

243 J. W. McMahon who had 4-210.

244 A. L. Hassett and D. G. Bradman who in the second match at The Oval scored 139 and 128 respectively.

245 He faced just two balls.

125

246 He was bowled without scoring by Eric Hollies of Warwickshire.

247 It brought his Test average just below 100 at 99.94.

248 Alec Bedser.

249 Len Hutton with 30 and 64.

250 Arthur Morris who was run out on 196.

1948—THE COUNTY SCENE

251 A. E. "Dusty" Rhodes who was playing for MCC.

252 H. S. Squires, A. J. McIntyre and E. R. T. Holmes.

253 Alec Bedser.

254 J. C. "Johnny" Clay.

255 J. W. McMahon.

256 Laurie Fishlock who in the first innings scored 253.

257 Jim Sims.

258 There were 35,000 spectators in the ground.

259 M. R. Barton.

260 Glamorgan took the title for the first time in their history.

MORE DOINGS OF 1948

261 T. H. Barling who became coach at Harrow.

262 Jim Laker.

263 The match was over in a day.

264 Ken Cranston.

265 D. G. W. Fletcher 108, E. A. Bedser 128.

266 Roly Jenkins who top scored with 81 in the Worcester second innings.

267 Kent.

268 J. V. Wilson.

269 G. N. G. Kirby.

270 Jack Young at The Oval in August 1948.

THE 1949 SEASON

271 The championship in 1949 was shared by Middlesex and Yorkshire and Surrey beat the former twice and the latter once.

272 Against Hampshire at The Oval. They were all out for 59 in

their second innings and Fishlock scored 123 in the only Surrey innings.

273 Stan Squires 210.

274 Alec Bedser 15.1-5-25-6 and J. F. Parker 15-4-19-4.

275 The Gloucestershire match. Tom Graveney and J. K. Graveney were the men.

276 It was J. K. Graveney's first county match.

277 P. Westerman.

278 M. H. Wrigley.

279 G. H. G. Doggart (Sussex), D. J. Insole (Essex), A. C. Burnett (Yorkshire), J. J. Warr (Middlesex).

280 Jim Laker and G. N. G. Kirby.

MORE FROM 1949

281 L. B. Fishlock 210 and E. A. Bedser 154*.

282 M. R. Barton who scored 101* in the first innings.

283 Johnny Wardle.

284 Eric Bedser 163 having just scored 154 against Somerset.

285 It was Surrey's first post-war win over their London rivals.

286 Bernard Constable.

287 Eric Hollies.

288 He took 21 wickets having had an analysis of 10-143 in the first match at Edgbaston.

289 D. S. Sheppard.

290 Roly Jenkins of Worcestershire. Astonishingly he had done the hat-trick against Surrey in 1948 also.

1950—A CALYPSO YEAR

291 Everton Weekes 232, Clyde Walcott 128.

292 Laurie Fishlock, 110 in the second innings.

293 M. R. Barton 99.

294 Roy Marshall 143.

295 Clyde Walcott 149.

296 Len Hutton who scored 202* in the first England innings.

297 Alf Valentine.

298 Alec Bedser.

299 Five.

300 Reg Simpson, David Sheppard, John Dewes, Trevor Bailey, Freddie Brown.

1950—THE COUNTY SCENE

301 Jim Laker.

302 Bernard Constable.

303 Ray Dovey.

304 In the match he took 13-75.

305 Roy Tattersall.

306 Vic Jackson who dismissed M. R. Barton, Alec Bedser and Stewart Surridge.

307 All 11 batsmen scored double figures.

308 It was so cold that waiting batsmen wore overcoats.

309 Ray Smith 6-142, Peter Smith 13-113.

310 R. Divecha.

MORE OF 1950

311 Tom Clark who made 175 in the match at The Oval in June.

312 Norman Horner.

313 Laurie Fishlock with 111 in the first innings against Middlesex.

314 Dennis Compton with 115* in the first innings.

315 Alec Bedser.

316 In the second innings he had a match-winning 57 in 50 minutes.

317 Jim Laker.

318 P. B. H. May 118.

319 N. W. D. Yardley 104.

320 A football match was played. Corinthians met an F.A. XI to mark the resumption of play at The Oval by Corinthian-Casuals.

THE YEAR 1951

321 Peter May.

322 Jim Laker 61, Alex Bedser 73.

323 Against Gloucestershire at Gloucester in July.

324 J. B. Statham.

325 Vic Jackson.

326 R. Routledge.

327 E. R. T. Holmes.

328 G. J. Whittaker 129 and W. S. Surridge 87.

329 Jack Ikin, 125* out of 197 all out.

330 It was their first win at The Oval since 1904.

THE YEAR 1952—MOSTLY BOWLING

331 At Llanelly against Glamorgan in June.

332 The same month against Gloucestershire at Bristol.

333 Peter May.

334 F. R. Brown.

335 Jim Laker.

336 Alec Bedser 11.4-2-23-6 and Stuart Surridge 11-2-26-3.

337 Laurie Fishlock and Jack Parker.

338 Leicestershire.

339 D. F. Cox

340 M. H. S. Stevenson.

1952 AND MOSTLY INDIANS

341 He was no-balled for throwing.

342 W. F. Price who formerly played for Middlesex.

343 R. V. Divecha in the Surrey first innings, his victims being
Whittaker, Laker and Alec Bedser.

344 He made 143 in the Surrey second innings and captained the
county side for the first time.

345 They slumped to 5-6.

346 F. S. Trueman 5-48 and A. V. Bedser 5-41.

347 D. S. Sheppard 119.

348 Len Hutton 86, D. S. Sheppard 119.

349 Surrey won by 141 runs.

350 G. S. Ramchand.

351 Stuart Surridge and Alec Bedser in Jack Ikin's benefit match.

352 Jack Parker with Freddie Brown against Kent at Blackheath in 1932, E. Whitfield against India at The Oval in 1932 and Alf Gover again versus India in 1936.

353 Warwickshire were bowled out in a day for 45 and 52.

354 Alec Bedser took 12 for 35.

355 Alan Brazier.

356 David Allen.

357 Peter Loader and Ramon Subba Row.

358 Jim McConnon.

359 Worcestershire out for 25 and 40, Surrey 92-3 declared.

360 Tony Lock.

JUST BEFORE THE CHAMPIONSHIP

361 D. S. Sheppard 141 and K. P. A. Matthews 77.

362 By scoring 151 in the first innings he reached 100 centuries.

363 J. V. "Vic" Wilson made 114.

364 L. Livingston 100 and F. Jakeman 176*.

365 W. G. Keighley 110.

366 In the Notts second innings he had a best-ever return of 8-18 and also reached 1000 first-class wickets, after only seven seasons.

367 Tony Lock.

368 Jack Bannister.

369 Ted Burgin.

370 Leicestershire.

THE CHAMPIONSHIP FIFTIES

371 C. H. Palmer, formerly of Worcestershire.

372 Bob Appleyard.

373 Ramon Subba Row.

374 J. M. Allan.

375 Surrey slumped to 6 for 4 wickets.

376 J. G. Dewes with 101* out of 203.

377 Tony Lock.

378 Alec Bedser.

379 Roy Marshall.

380 Tom Clark who scored 191 v. Kent at Blackheath and 190 against Gloucestershire at The Oval.

W. S. SURRIDGE

381 In 1947.

382 Emmanuel.

383 In Wisden 1953.

384 Alfred Shaw of Nottinghamshire and Brian Sellers of Yorkshire.

385 The county programme was completed without a single match being drawn.

386 In 1952 when he took 58 catches.

387 He took 501 wickets in first-class matches.

388 He stayed in the same hotel as the rest of the side.

389 101 matches were won in this period.

390 There were 27 losses only.

KEN BARRINGTON

391 As a leg-spin bowler.

392 In 1955 against South Africa.

393 For four years, against India in 1959.

394 Twenty altogether, six in England and fourteen abroad.

395 He has made a century on each of the six English Test grounds and against every country which was then playing Test cricket (all bar Sri Lanka of the present countries).

396 In his career he took 273 wickets at 32.61.

397 He was dropped for having taken seven and a half hours to score his 137.

398 Walter Hammond in 1928-29, 1553 runs at 91.35.

399 Herbert Sutcliffe with an average of 66.85.

400 He did not make a century against Derbyshire, Glamorgan, Somerset or Sussex.

401 Twice, he took 216 wickets in 1955 and 212 in 1957.

402 On one occasion against Kent at Blackheath in 1956, 10-54.

403 A low roof in an indoor bowling school caused him to lower his arm.

404 W. F. "Fred" Price.

405 He was the Middlesex wicket-keeper between 1926 and 1947.

406 Christmas.

407 Yes, in the mid 1930s he made some 40 appearances for the county.

408 The square was ready for play by 15 April.

409 45,000 turves were brought from Hoo in Kent.

410 He was made Inspector of Pitches for the whole country.

TWO OPENERS CLARK AND PARKER

411 Aston Villa and Walsall.

412 From 1952-59 almost exactly coinciding with the championship years.

413 He made 191 against Kent at Blackheath in 1956.

414 He made 11,490 runs at 26.39 and hit 12 centuries.

415 Jack Parker never actually played for England but had been selected to go on the 1939 tour of India which was cancelled on the outbreak of war.

416 He headed the Surrey bowling averages in 1946 and the batting averages the following season.

417 His highest score was 255 against the New Zealanders in 1949.

418 He scored 14,272 runs at 31.58.

419 He took 543 wickets at 28.87.

420 He did not score his first century until 1938.

THE HEAVENLY TWINS, THE BEDSERS

421 At Reading.

422 From 1939-1960.

423 11 times.

424 D. G. W. Fletcher.

425 Both played twice in 1939 but not in the county championship.
426 They took part in the evacuation of Dunkirk.
427 11 in each of his first two Tests against India in 1946.
428 In the first innings he took 7-49, the best record for a bowler on his Test debut for England.
429 In the first innings Eric took 7-99 and in the second Alec 8-42.
430 In his early days Eric normally wore a cap when batting. In the field he turned up the bottom of his sweater.

P. B. H. MAY

431 In 66 Tests.
432 Frank Woolley of Kent.
433 13.
434 Association football and a half-blue for Eton fives.
435 The Fives Amateur Championship.
436 W. S. Surridge.
437 Two, those of 1957 and 1958.
438 Against the *Evening Standard*, successfully.
439 He led England on 41 occasions.
440 Pegasus, the side drawn from Oxbridge players.

BERNARD CONSTABLE

441 He was the last pre-war player to appear regularly in post World War II cricket.
442 Against West Indies at The Oval in July 1939.
443 Against Lancashire at Old Trafford on 30 August 1939. The game was given up after two days on account of the political situation.
444 Against the Combined Services in 1946.
445 A leg-break bowler.
446 Against Somerset, 205* at The Oval.
447 East Molesey.
448 In 1938.
449 Against Yorkshire, scoring 154* at The Oval and 100 at Leeds.
450 He made 109 in the first innings.

JOHN EDRICH

451 With Norfolk, his home county.

452 Three, Geoff, Brian and Eric all played county cricket.

453 100* for Combined Services against Hampshire.

454 Against Worcestershire at The Oval in 1958.

455 112 and 124 against Nottinghamshire at Trent Bridge in 1959.

456 Against Australia, 120 at Lord's in 1964.

457 77.

458 103.

459 1311 runs.

460 Six, including one triple and a double century. He was also out twice in the 90s.

JIM LAKER'S FIFTEEN

461 *Over To Me.*

462 With Catford Cricket Club.

463 In the Test Trial, England v. The Rest at Bradford, 1950.

464 Saltaire Cricket Club.

465 Against the Combined Services at The Oval, 1946.

466 In Barbados in the West Indian tour of 1947-48. He took 7-103 in the innings, the last 6 for 25.

467 Against Australia at Trent Bridge in 1948, 63 out of 165 all out.

468 He took ten wickets for 119 runs.

469 No, 17 wickets is the next best tally.

470 Yes, he was selected to go there in 1958-59.

471 He was 13 years at The Oval.

472 He took 100 wickets 11 times.

473 He played some 30 games for Essex as an amateur over three seasons.

474 In first-class cricket he scored 7304 runs.

475 He made two centuries, both for Surrey.

THE 1960S

476 Stewart Storey with 100 in 98 minutes against Somerset at Taunton.

477 Western Australia.

478 Bedfordshire.

479 Wicket-keeper Roy Swetman.

480 Peter May and the Bedser brothers.

481 1962, although he played occasionally afterwards.

482 M. D. Willett.

483 M. J. Stewart.

484 Jim Standen of West Ham United who took 5-14 for Worcestershire against Surrey.

485 They asked Kent for a move from Blackheath and the away game took place at Gravesend.

STILL WITH THE SWINGING, SPINNING SIXTIES

486 D. A. D. Sydenham.

487 A. B. D. Parsons, Peter Loader and Tony Lock.

488 In January 1969.

489 Batsman Nick Cosh.

490 Richard Jefferson and Stewart Storey.

491 David Halfyard. Later still he played for Notts.

492 M. Willett.

493 In March 1965.

494 John Edrich and Ken Barrington.

495 For Surrey against the New Zealanders.

AROUND THE 1970S

496 Dudley Owen-Thomas.

497 Chris Old.

498 They ran a six!

499 Graham Johnson of Kent.

500 Alan Butcher 8-5-10-1 and Pat Pocock 8-2-16-3.

501 Geoff Arnold.

502 Because Surrey batting first had made 254-7 and Somerset's 257-5 was the highest-ever total recorded by a side batting second in this trophy.

503 Peter Denning who made 112.

504 Younis Ahmed.

505 Malcolm Nash.

MAY AND STEWART

506 Peter Barker Howard.

507 He scored a century in his first Test and a century for Gentlemen against Players.

508 He scored 2339 runs at an average of 68.79.

509 George Geary formerly of Leicestershire.

510 Against Hampshire in 1950.

511 He held 77 catches, a county record for Surrey and only one less than the all-time record of Walter Hammond.

512 He took seven catches in an innings at Northampton.

513 Against Pakistan in 1954.

514 Charlton Athletic.

515 The FA Amateur Cup final replay at Ayresome Park Middlesbrough.

THE YEAR 1976

516 Sadiq Mohammed 117 and Andy Stovold 123.

517 Against Hampshire at Bournemouth when he dismissed Greenidge and Richards.

518 Herbert Strudwick's record of 1493 victims behind the stumps.

519 C. J. Aworth.

520 Owen Dudley-Thomas.

521 Ray Illingworth.

522 Richard Lumb 118 and John Hampshire 127.

523 Robin Jackman.

524 Chris Waller.

525 Younis Ahmed who would later play for Worcester, 183* and 59.

THE YEAR 1974

526 Abid Ali who took 6-23 and also made 38*.

136

527 S. J. Storey.

528 Against Essex at Ilford.

529 Derek Underwood.

530 With 12 successive maiden overs being bowled to Derek Underwood and J. N. Graham, the last Kent pair.

531 Geoff Arnold who in the match took 9-77.

532 Freddie Titmus.

533 Phil Edmonds.

534 S. J. Storey and M. J. Edwards.

535 Geoff Arnold.

MORE OF 1974

536 R. D. V. Knight 100*.

537 Geoff Arnold.

538 J. D. Morley with 82* out of 237.

539 Geoff Boycott 142*.

540 Phil Carrick.

541 Younis Ahmed 101*.

542 Leicestershire.

543 John Edrich who scored 40 but got the award for his captaincy.

544 Ken Higgs of Leicestershire.

545 Intikhab Alam.

1973 TOURISTS AND COUNTIES

546 John Edrich 110.

547 Ian Chappell 101.

548 Ian Chappell made 118 and Greg Chappell 113. Brothers had never before made centuries in the same innings of a Test match.

549 Alan Knott 127* and 118*.

550 M. J. Edwards 121.

551 Barry Dudleston.

552 David Steele 131, Mushtaq Mohammed 120.

553 Tom Cartwright.

554 Majid Khan who made 139 in the first innings.

137

555 John Edrich 127* (96 in the first innings) and Younis 143 for Surrey and Peter Parfitt 129 for Middlesex.

MORE OF 1973

556 Dudley Owen-Thomas 100*.
557 Yorkshire by an innings and 12 runs.
558 Intikhab Alam.
559 Majid Khan, 204 in the first innings.
560 Roy Fredericks, 107 in the second innings.
561 He took four wickets in five balls and there was a run-out off the last ball of the over.
562 Five, the victims being Fletcher, Turner, Hobbs, Edmeades and Lever.
563 Gordon Greenidge 57 and Roy Marshall 51.
564 Garfield Sobers.
565 John Snow.

STILL MORE 1973

566 Mickey Stewart who was made Man of the Match.
567 Norman Gifford.
568 Basil D'Oliveira who made 45* and bowled 10-2-17-3.
569 Younis Ahmed 141.
570 He had become only the seventh man to score 1000 runs before the end of May.
571 Stuart Storey 107 and Robin Jackman 83*.
572 His 100* was his 100th first-class century.
573 Geoff Howarth 159.
574 Hedley.
575 Robin Jackman.

1973 BUSY OLD YEAR

576 For Surrey Intikhab Alam made 139 and for Gloucestershire Zaheer Abbas scored 153* in the first innings and Sadiq Mohammed 116* in the second. In addition Younis Ahmed made 76 and 56 for Surrey.

577 Yorkshire.

578 Pat Pocock.

579 Colin Milburn who scored 57 in the second innings. He had lost an eye in a car crash.

580 Intikhab who scored exactly 100.

581 Robin Jackman, his victims being Howard Cooper, Mike Bore and Geoff Cope.

582 John Edrich 74 and Graham Roope 115*.

583 Bernard Julian.

584 Against Worcestershire at Byfleet, Surrey 200-4 in reply to 200-7.

585 For Worcestershire Basil D'Oliveira scored 100 and for Surrey Graham Roope had 120*.

ROBIN D. JACKMAN

586 He was born in Simla in India.

587 He was not allowed entry to Guyana.

588 Robin David.

589 He was Cricketer of the Year in the 1981 edition of Wisden.

590 He took 121 first-class wickets in 1980.

591 Of these 114 were championship wickets.

592 Patrick Cargill.

593 He topped both the batting and bowling averages.

594 He joined Surrey in 1964.

595 Six years later, in 1970.

THE 1979 SEASON

596 Pat Pocock.

597 M. J. Procter whose 100 came in 76 minutes.

598 R. D. V. Knight.

599 The final ball went for a bye.

600 Pat Pocock again.

601 Alan Butcher 103 and Graham Clinton 120.

602 Roger Knight.

603 The adhesive John Emburey.

604 Roger Knight, 183 and 17*.

605 The match against Sussex at The Oval in August. Sussex captain Arnold Long felt that as Alan Butcher had been ill before the match he ought not to have been selected. He refused to allow him to resume at the fall of the fifth wicket, Butcher having left the field at 26-0.

FURTHER EVENTS OF 1979

606 Graham Clinton who made 134 against Kent.

607 Younis Ahmed who made 107.

608 Jim Cumbes.

609 Arnold Long, Geoff Arnold, Chris Waller.

610 Younis Ahmed who also reached three figures in the Benson and Hedges match between the two counties.

611 They lost to Essex by 35 runs.

612 Graham Gooch scored 120 for Essex.

613 Sadiq Mohammed 58 and Zaheer Abbas 60*.

614 Against Essex, Surrey were 88 all out and Essex were coasting at 25-1.

615 In both years the county defeated the visiting Australian tourists.

SEASON 1977

616 He was picked as twelfth man for the First Test in 1971 but was not selected for the Surrey side for the next county match.

617 In August 1969, he topped the bowling averages with 17 wickets at 19.3.

618 Robin Jackman and Geoff Arnold.

619 Graham Roope who scored 107 in the match in May.

620 By coincidence he was at the other end when both Geoff Boycott and John Edrich completed their 100th centuries.

621 Keith Fletcher and Graham Roope respectively.

622 John Edrich 90 and Alan Butcher 112.

623 Gordon Greenidge 108 and Trevor Jesty 111*.

624 The game with Kent at Maidstone. All the Surrey side except the wicket-keeper bowled in the second innings.

625 Graham Roope with 110*.

MORE OF 1977

626 Viv Richards 204 and Peter Roebuck 112.
627 G. P. Howarth 110.
628 He was the 17th player to do this.
629 Three, Hobbs, Hayward and Sandham.
630 Ken Shuttleworth.
631 Jack Birkenshaw.
632 Gordon Greenidge, 64 and 200*.
633 Geoff Arnold.
634 Bob Willis.
635 Peter Lee.

THE SEASON OF 1978

636 S. S. Surridge, son of W. S. Surridge kept wicket, took one
     catch and made 2*.
637 A. J. Harvey-Walker.
638 Nigel Cowley.
639 G. W. Johnson.
640 They were 16th in the championship.
641 Mike Selvey, for Middlesex.
642 David Smith and Monte Lynch.
643 Derek Underwood of Kent.
644 He took 13-64 at The Oval.
645 Chris Tavaré.

MORE 1978s

646 Alan Butcher 176 and Roger Knight 119.
647 Roger Knight 128.
648 Tony Pigott of Sussex at Hove in July.
649 Glenn Turner 150 and Alan Ormrod 173.
650 A. J. Hignell, later of Gloucestershire, 108 and 145.
651 Roger Prideaux later of Kent and Northants.

141

652 Barnsley.

653 Pat Pocock 8-2-13-2 and Intikhab 8-0-23-2.

654 25 runs; Intikhab took three wickets and Pocock one.

655 Wayne Larkins, who hit 107 in 74 minutes.

THE LATE 1970s

656 Keppler Wessels, Javed Miandad, Gehan Mendis.

657 P. B. Wight. The first day was washed out and a late decision was taken to play on the second day by which time the other umpire, Cec Pepper, was unable to be contacted, having left the ground.

658 R. D. V. Knight for Sussex at The Oval.

659 Graham Roope.

660 Trevor Jesty who made 107.

661 David Gower 79* and Roger Tolchard 67*.

662 The BAC ground at Byfleet.

663 Basharat Hassan.

664 The match against Sussex at The Oval.

665 The first five Sussex batsmen each recorded a duck.

PAT POCOCK

666 He is Welsh, born at Bangor in Caernarvonshire.

667 Percy.

668 Eight years.

669 No, his highest score is 75* against Notts in 1968.

670 No, his best was 9-57 against Glamorgan at Cardiff in 1979.

671 He was never picked for a tour of Australia.

672 He took four wickets in four balls, six wickets in nine balls and seven wickets in eleven balls.

673 In 1967.

674 On seven occasions.

675 W. G. Grace's mother was a Pocock, a distant relation of the Surrey player.

676 Ian Payne who went to Gloucestershire.

677 Pat Pocock.

678 David M. Smith.

679 Surrey, Worcestershire and Glamorgan.

680 Saeed Ahmed.

681 Yes. He had two matches for Pakistan.

682 Fourteen years, four months.

683 In 1965.

684 He has scored 43 centuries.

685 4-10 against Cambridge University at Fenners in 1975.

686 Kim Hughes with Watsonians and Ashley Mallett with Ayr.

687 Ray East.

688 Robin Jackman took 8-58.

689 Clive Radley 136, Mike Gatting 136.

690 Roger Knight.

691 R. G. H. Cheatle.

692 Sylvester Clarke.

693 Sylvester Clarke 4-29 and Robin Jackman 6-30.

694 He had then taken five wickets in an innings against each of the other 16 counties.

695 Alan Butcher with 216*.

696 G. S. Clinton 89.

697 In the first-round match against Northants at The Oval.

698 Against Essex in the quarter-final at Chelmsford.

699 Robin Jackman.

700 There were 24 extras, nine byes, five leg-byes, six wides and four no-balls.

701 Mike Brearley with 96*.

702 M. W. W. Selvey.

703 Vincent van der Bijl.

704 Sylvester Clarke.

705 David Turner.

THE YEAR 1981

706 David Graveney.

707 Against Hampshire at Portsmouth in July.

708 Sylvester Clarke.

709 John Emburey.

710 Clive Rice.

711 Intikhab Alam.

712 West of Scotland Cricket Club in Glasgow.

713 Younis Ahmed.

714 Monte Lynch.

715 K. B. S. Jarvis.

THE 1982 SEASON

716 P. N. Kirsten 164*, 123*.

717 Andy Needham.

718 Robin Jackman.

719 He was not selected, having been dropped for over-celebrating!

720 Fred Titmus.

721 He took the last three wickets in the match.

722 He was 49 and had first played in county cricket in 1949.

723 Sylvester Clarke.

724 Graham Roope.

725 Malcolm Marshall who took 7-38.

THE YEAR 1983

726 Surrey were all out for 14 runs.

727 Norbert Phillip 7.3-4-4-6 and Neil Foster 7-3-10-4.

728 Roger Knight 101*.

729 Alan Butcher 128 and Dave Smith 131*.

730 Viv Richards 142* and 76.

731 Jeremy Lloyds.

732 David Hughes.

733 Alec Stewart 118*.

734 His father Micky was twelfth man and father and son fielded together for a short time.

735 Jack Richards. The next highest score for Gloucestershire was 21.

THE YEAR 1984

736 Against Essex at Chelmsford in May. In a match reduced to one day Surrey batted for 88 overs and did not declare.

737 Keith Fletcher for Essex and Alan Butcher for Surrey.

738 He made 142 against Gloucestershire at Cheltenham.

739 Terry Alderman.

740 Surrey v. Lancashire at Old Trafford where Jack Simmons took 10-156 and Pat Pocock 10-167.

741 Andy Needham.

742 Peter Such.

743 Roger Knight.

744 Yorkshire.

745 Alan Butcher 117*, 114.

RECENT EVENTS

746 Duncan Pauline.

747 Sylvester Clarke.

748 Dave Thomas, 119.

749 Ian R. Payne.

750 Dermot Reeve who took 3-51 and made 119.

751 Graham Clinton 113* out of 260.

752 Graham Monkhouse 100*.

753 Alan Butcher 118 and Graham Clinton 192 who put on 277.

754 No, Hobbs and Hayward made 290 for the first wicket against Yorkshire in 1914 but that match was played at Lord's because The Oval had been requisitioned because of the impending outbreak of war.

755 N. J. Falkner 101* and K. T. Medlycott 117*.

THE YEAR 1986

756 Alan Butcher.
757 Pat Pocock.
758 At Chelmsford against Essex.
759 Jeremy Lloyds.
760 Pat Pocock after Surrey had lost by an innings and 193 runs to Hampshire at Basingstoke.
761 Nick Falkner made 102 and Keith Medlycott took 10-155.
762 Richard Hadlee.
763 Trevor Jesty.
764 Tony Gray in for Sylvester Clarke.
765 Kent.

IN AND OUT

766 All are bowlers, all started with Surrey, all played for England.
767 Yes, 102 against Middlesex at Lord's in 1986.
768 Trevor Jesty.
769 Hampshire.
770 Ten years.
771 Monte Lynch in August 1977 v. Middlesex.
772 Lynch has twice damaged Knight's car while batting with enormous sixes.
773 Glamorgan, 141* in 88 minutes at Guildford in 1982 and the previous season at Swansea he took 3-6.
774 Keith Medlycott who scored 117* against Cambridge University.
775 Banstead.

ENEMY DEEDS

776 Norman Cowans.
777 Chris Cowdrey.
778 Gordon Greenidge, 5-49 at Southampton in 1971.
779 Simon Hughes.
780 Paul Jarvis.

781 Dermot Reeve of Sussex, 119.
782 David Turner.
783 D. M. Ward.
784 Mike Watkinson.
785 A. J. Wright of Gloucestershire.

PACEMAN AND KEEPER

786 Trinidad.
787 Against Yorkshire at Sheffield.
788 His analysis was 8-40.
789 Jack Crapp of Gloucestershire and J. "Pasty" Harris of Nottinghamshire.
790 Nottinghamshire.
791 He has taken five wickets.
792 Jack Russell of Gloucestershire.
793 Bruce French.
794 Perth.
795 Roy Swetman in the 1950s.

EIGHTIES ROUND UP

796 R. J. Hadlee.
797 Monte Lynch on the car of Roger Knight.
798 Both men scored centuries.
799 Rodney Ontong.
800 Allan Border.
801 Gloucester 'keeper Robert "Jack" Russell took three catches off three consecutive balls to get rid of Stewart, Butcher and Lynch.
802 Only once, G. O. Dawkes doing it for Derbyshire v. Worcestershire in 1958.
803 Russell scored 71 in the Gloucestershire first innings and Richards in the first innings for Surrey had 115.
804 Pat Pocock.
805 Graham Clinton who made 84* out of 161.

147

CURRENT AND RECENT PERFORMERS

806 Neil, who has played for the second XI.

807 Nick Taylor who turned out for Yorkshire, Surrey and Somerset.

808 Martin Bicknell.

809 Graham Elliott Brown.

810 Nick Falkner.

811 Dave Thomas.

812 Fastest 100 of the season in 62 minutes against Glamorgan at Swansea.

813 Gully.

814 Fred Titmus was responsible for his signing.

815 Nottinghamshire.

THE 1986 SEASON

816 Martin Bicknell.

817 Graham Elliott Brown.

818 Alan Butcher.

819 His brother Ian is with Leicestershire.

820 He scored a century, before lunch against Glamorgan at The Oval in 1980.

821 Graham Monkhouse.

822 He had one first-class century 100* against Kent at The Oval in 1984.

823 Andy Needham.

824 D. B. Pauline.

825 Alex Stewart and S. S. Surridge.

INDIVIDUAL HAPPENINGS

826 R. I. Jefferson of Winchester and Cambridge University.

827 The very disappointing sum of just over £4000.

828 He had to have an operation on a knee-cap.

829 Against Derbyshire at The Oval in July 1977.

830 It was his 945th first-class innings.

831 Against Worcestershire back in 1958.

832 He scored seven centuries against the Australians, three in Britain and four in Australia.

833 N. H. Bennett.

834 M. R. Barton of Oxford University.

835 Stan Squires.

836 H. O. Bloomfield whose average is therefore 169.

837 He scored 39 centuries.

838 On nine occasions.

839 He accomplished this twice.

840 He took 437 wickets and held 281 catches.

841 J. A. Newman who scored 102 and 102*.

842 Joe O'Gorman of the brothers act, Dave and Joe O'Gorman.

843 Andrew Sandham.

844 With his very first ball he took the wicket of W. E. Bates, the Glamorgan opener.

845 He scored two centuries, both at The Oval in 1905.

REALLY MIXED GRILL

846 Arnold Dyson.

847 A. H. H. Gilligan.

848 Challen Hasler Lufkin Skeet.

849 S. A. Block.

850 Robin Jackman 5-22 in the last match of the season v. Yorkshire.

851 Paul Pridgeon who took 6-26.

852 J. M. Kelly.

853 Major D. G. Foster.

854 Wally Keeton who made 312.

855 Lord's was required for the Eton-Harrow match!

856 Billy Beldham.

857 Bobby Abel.

858 Jack Hobbs.

859 Andrew Sandham.

860 D. L. A. Jephson.

861 W. C. "Razor" Smith.

862 G. G. Arnold.

863 Ken Barrington.

864 N. Wanostrocht.

865 H. D. Leveson-Gower.

CURIOSITIES

866 J. H. "Danny" Meyer.

867 Hobbs, Sandham, Ducat, Shepherd, Barling, Peach and Fender.

868 O. J. Wait.

869 Denis Hill-Wood.

870 Gladstone Small.

871 It was his fifth half-century in seven innings against Surrey and he became only the third man to make 1000 J.P.L. runs for two counties.

872 Brian Castor.

873 51 years.

874 He was given out because he hit the ball twice and ran.

875 Derek Pringle.

ODDS AND ENDS

876 Thomas McMurray.

877 H. S. Altham.

878 J. B. King, the famous American cricketer from Philadelphia.

879 Walter Monckton.

880 G. F. Earle.

881 H. C. McDonell.

882 S. E. Busher. Grace was dismissed for 2 and 0 in 1908 playing in a game which was interrupted by snow.

883 Arnold Long took 11 catches behind the stumps in the match.

884 Against Surrey for Cambridge in 1904. The University still lost.

885 In 1897 Surrey declined to meet Middlesex "if Sir Timothy O'Brien play". He never took the field against them again.

MIXED BAG

886 F. R. Brown and R. Subba Row.

887 Hayes, Hayward, Hitch and Hobbs.

888 He wore particularly long and baggy trousers.

889 Sandy Tait.

890 Peter Loader against West Indies at Headingley.

891 There was Sunday play in five matches.

892 Bert Lock.

893 In the 1967 season.

894 David Gibson.

895 F. R. Brown, once for Surrey and once for Northants.

GENERAL POST

896 In 1845.

897 The Prince of Wales. The ground belongs to the Duchy of Cornwall.

898 George Lohmann.

899 He died at an early age in South Africa of consumption.

900 Tom Richardson.

901 W. H. "Bill" Lockwood.

902 Charles Alcock.

903 The Australian XI of 1878.

904 The Australian team of 1880.

905 The four are Hayward, Hobbs, Sandham and Edrich.

906 N. A. Knox.

907 He was so called because he was extremely thin.

908 Tom Rushby.

909 Tom Rushby 5-9 and W. Smith 5-12.

910 V. F. S. Crawford.

911 Andrew Sandham as player, coach and scorer.

912 W. S. Surridge.

913 For five years, winning the championship every year.

914 He was never picked for Gentlemen versus Players oddly enough.

915 Since 1912 when Hampshire defeated the tourists.

HERE AND THERE

916 Jim Laker.

917 Bernard Constable 109 in the first innings.

918 He presented his Australian cap to Stuart Surridge.

919 Albert Craig who used to compose impromptu verses and sell them to the spectators.

920 Arnold Long, Nick Majendie, Arthur McIntyre and O. D. Kember.

921 Alfred Jeacocke.

922 Eight centuries and six appearances for the Gentlemen.

923 Alan Peach.

924 Tom Rushby with 6-67 and J. N. Crawford with 11-63. Sussex were all out for 43 and 90.

925 J. N. Crawford with H. C. McDonnell at Cheltenham in 1904 against Gloucestershire. The latter took 10-89 and Crawford 10-78.

ODDITIES

926 Gilbert "Gilly" Reay.

927 Lord Tedder.

928 S. J. McCabe.

929 Hobbs and Sandham, 428 against Oxford University in 1926, Hobbs 261, Sandham 183.

930 1931 when he headed the Surrey bowling averages with 57 wickets at 18.47.

931 George W. Beldam.

932 It appears to have been the first-ever by a left-handed Surrey batsman in championship cricket.

933 R. J. O. Meyer, later captain of Somerset. Playing for Cambridge he pulled a ball from Fender for four. It touched the wicket and the bail spun round at right angles but stayed on. He was given out because the bail had to be replaced before play could continue. MCC later ruled this decision erroneous.

934 South of the Border.

935 Graham Clinton.

FINAL LOOK ROUND

936 To commemorate the recent death of Jim Laker, the great Surrey and England slow bowler.

937 Martin Bicknell.

938 Monte Lynch.

939 Trevor Jesty.

940 Not unless there are exceptional circumstances.

941 He survived five balls against Nottinghamshire so that Surrey rose from sixth to second in the final championship placings.

942 In 1979.

943 Pat Pocock.

944 He took 5-17 in 12 overs and made 55.

945 D. N. Patel 132*.

PICTORIAL QUIZ NUMBER ONE

946 Intikhab Alam in action against the Australians.

947 Roger Knight.

948 David Smith.

949 Stuart Surridge.

950 Percy Fender.

951 From left to right — Harold Larwood, Bill Voce, Ken Archer, George Mann, Gubby Allen and Keith Miller.

952 Colin Cowdrey and Bobby Simpson.

953 Alan Butcher who scored a century before lunch against Glamorgan in 1980. No Surrey player had done this since Jack Hobbs in 1927.

954 Three, Ken Barrington and Tony Lock (third and second right back row) and John Edrich (centre of front row).

955 Graham Roope and Robin Jackman.

PICTORIAL QUIZ NUMBER TWO

956 Geoff Arnold.

957 Sylvester Clarke and Jack Richards trudging wearily off at Guildford.

958 Geoff Howarth, the New Zealand Test player and captain.

959 Another great Surrey stalwart, Jim Laker.

960 From left to right the three are Frank Muir (behind Jim Laker), Dorothy Tutin and Robert Powell.

961 Pat Pocock.

962 Bob Willis who ended up with Warwickshire.

963 Alec Stewart, son of Mickey Stewart.

964 Graham Clinton who came to The Oval from Kent.

965 Roger Knight at Cheltenham making 142 against his former county (or one of them), Gloucestershire.

PICTORIAL QUIZ NUMBER THREE

966 Roy Swetman is the keeper and Ken Barrington is in the slips.

967 Sid Buller.

968 John Edrich taking hasty evasive action against Fred Trueman.

969 Yorkshire; the turning wicket-keeper is Jimmy Binks.

970 Roy Swetman in his England cap.

971 Ramon Subba Row who later captained Northamptonshire.

972 N. S. Tamhane.

973 A. H. "Tony" Gray.

974 Andy Needham.

975 Dave Thomas.

976 K. J. Key and J. Shuter, back and centre rows respectively.
977 E. T. A. Wilkinson.
978 G. A. Lohmann.
979 Tom Richardson.
980 Bobby Abel.
981 Tom Hayward.
982 Hobbs and Sandham.
983 Fishlock and Gregory.
984 E. W. Brooks, T. H. Barling, H. S. Squires and R. J. Gregory.
985 H. M. Garland-Wells.
986 M. J. C. Allom.

PICTORIAL QUIZ NUMBER FIVE

987 Percy Fender.
988 Douglas Jardine.
989 E. R. T. Holmes.
990 Stuart Surridge.
991 Essex at The Oval.
992 Alf Gover.
993 Freddie Brown of Surrey, Northants and England.
994 The Alec one — A. V. Bedser.
995 Peter May.
996 Alf Gover is the presenter and Arthur McIntyre the recipient.

PICTORIAL QUIZ NUMBER SIX

997 Marshal of the Royal Air Force, Lord Tedder.
998 To commemorate his taking 10-88 against the Australians at The Oval in May 1956.
999 He took all ten in an innings in the Old Trafford Test that summer.
1000 The Surrey captain, H. M. Garland-Wells.
1001 Peter May, Alec Bedser and Arthur McIntyre.
1002 Top to bottom: Tony Lock, Mickey Stewart and Stuart Surridge.

1003 Brian Castor.

1004 Herbert Strudwick.

1005 A. J. "Sandy" Tait.

1006 There are nine, to wit, standing left to right: Barrington, Lock, Loader, Stewart, Laker, Swetman and sitting Alec Bedser, May and McIntyre.

PICTORIAL QUIZ SEVEN

1007 David Gower congratulates Jack Richards after the latter's maiden Test century at Perth against Australia in 1987.

1008 Martin Bicknell.

1009 Laurie Fishlock.

1010 J. Firth.

1011 Trevor Jesty, formerly of Hampshire.

1012 Australian Rules Football, Carlton v. North Melbourne.

1013 Surrey got it for fastest scoring rate. Graeme Hick of Worcestershire is centre stage, John Lever of Essex on the right.